LITERATURE ANTHOLOGIES

P9-CAM-584

**A Collection of Prose and Poetry
on the Theme of**

VALUES

Edited by
Michael Spring
Editor, Literary Cavalcade

SCHOLASTIC INC.

CURRICULUM CONSULTANTS

Ms. Jo-Ann Lynn Mullen
Associate Professor of Education
Assistant Director, Division of
Education Studies
University of Northern Colorado
Greeley, Colorado

Ms. Gaylene Pepe
Department Head, English
Colonia Senior High School
Colonia, New Jersey

STAFF

Editorial Director:	Eleanor Angeles
Project Editor:	Michael Spring
Art Director:	Joe Borzetta
Assistant Editor:	Bette Birnbaum
Contributing Consultant:	Adrienne Betz
Editorial Assistant:	Karen Salazar

COVER ART: "Icare" by Henri Matisse. / Jazz ed. Verve, 1947. © SPADM, Paris/ VAGA, New York, 1985.

ISBN 0-590-34585-0

ACKNOWLEDGMENTS

Grateful acknowledgment is made to the following authors and publishers for the use of copyrighted materials. Every effort has been made to obtain permission to use previously published material. Any errors or omissions are unintentional.

Devin Adair for "Trees" from ALL NATURE IS MY BRIDE by Henry David Thoreau.
Atheneum Publishers, Inc. for "Quality" from AND MORE BY ANDY ROONEY. Copyright © 1982 Essay Productions. "The Country's Going Through a Dry Spell" from AMERICAN BEAT by Bob Greene. Copyright © 1983 John Deadline Enterprises.
David J. Blow for an edited version of "Wasteland" by Marya Mannes.
Joan Daves for "A Drum Major for Justice" by Martin Luther King, Jr. Copyright © 1968 by Martin Luther King, Jr.
Delacorte Press/Seymour Lawrence for "The Lie" from WELCOME TO THE MONKEY HOUSE by Kurt Vonnegut, Jr. Copyright © 1962 by Kurt Vonnegut, Jr. Originally published in SATURDAY EVENING POST.
Mari Evans for "The Silver Cell" from I AM A BLACK WOMAN by Mari Evans. Copyright © 1970 by Mari Evans.
Farrar, Straus & Giroux, Inc. for "The Washwoman" from A DAY OF PLEASURE by Isaac Bashevis Singer. Copyright 1962, 1965, 1966, 1969 by Isaac Bashevis Singer.
David Godine for "The Delight Song of Tsoai-talee" from ANGLE OF GEESE AND OTHERS POEMS by N. Scott Momaday. Copyright © 1974 by N. Scott Momaday.
Harcourt Brace Jovanovich, Inc. for "To a Siberian Woodsman," reprinted from OPENINGS by Wendell Berry. Copyright © 1968 by Wendell Berry.
Harper & Row, Publishers, Inc. for "How Many, How Much" from A LIGHT IN THE ATTIC: The Poems and Drawings of Shel Silverstein. Copyright © 1981 by Snake Eye Music, Inc. Excerpts from BLUE COLLAR JOURNAL by John Coleman (J. B. Lippincott Company). Copyright © 1974 by John Coleman.
Indiana University Press for "Once Upon a Time" by Gabriel Okara, from POEMS FROM BLACK AFRICA, edited by Langston Hughes.
Alfred A. Knopf, Inc. for "To Be of Use," reprinted from CIRCLES ON THE WATER by Marge Piercy. Copyright © 1972 by Marge Piercy. "Peace" from THE PANTHER AND THE LASH: POEMS OF OUR TIMES, by Langston Hughes. Copyright © 1967 by Arna Bontemps and George Houston Bass.
Little, Brown and Company for "The Gift and the Giver" from THE LION'S WHISKERS by Russell G. Davis and Brent K. Ashabranner. Copyright © 1959 by Russell G. Davis and Brent K. Ashabranner.
Macmillan Publishing Company for "Barter" by Sara Teasdale. Copyright 1917 by Macmillan Publishing Company, renewed 1945 by Mamie T. Wheless.
Pantheon Books, a division of Random House, Inc., for excerpts from AMERICAN DREAMS: LOST AND FOUND, by Studs Terkel. Copyright © 1980 by Studs Terkel.
The Putnam Publishing Group for "Being Somebody" from MEDIASPEAK: HOW TELEVISION MAKES UP YOUR MIND by Donna Woolfolk Cross. Copyright © 1983 by Donna Woolfolk Cross. "Scholastis Adolescum" by Art Buchwald from SON OF THE GREAT SOCIETY. Copyright © 1965, 1966 by Art Buchwald.
Real People Press for "Notes to Myself: Values" from NOTES TO MYSELF by Hugh Prather. © 1970 Real People Press.
St. Martin's Press, Incorporated and **The Reader's Digest Association, Inc.** for "Night of the Hunt Ball," reprinted from the book, THE BEST OF JAMES HERRIOT, copyright © 1982 by the Reader's Digest Association, Inc.; copyright © 1976, 1977 by James Herriot.
Scholastic Inc for "Ariel" by Sara Booth.
Scott Meredith Literary Agency, Inc., 845 Third Avenue, New York, NY 10022, for "Twelve Things I Wish They Taught at School" by Carl Sagan. Copyright © 1985 by Carl Sagan.
Simon & Schuster, Inc. for "Printer's Measure" from TELEVISION PLAYS by Paddy Chayefsky. Copyright © 1955 by Paddy Chayefsky, renewed © 1983 by Susan Chayefsky.
Beatriz de Tellez for "Just Lather, That's All" by Hernando Tellez (translated by Donald Yates). Copyright 1950 by Hernando Tellez from ASHES FOR THE WIND AND OTHER TALES.
University of New Mexico for excerpts from THE OLD ONES OF NEW MEXICO by Robert Coles. © 1973, Robert Coles.
Viking Penguin Inc. for an edited version of "The Lie Detector" from LATE NIGHT THOUGHTS ON LISTENING TO MAHLER'S NINTH by Lewis Thomas. Copyright © 1980, 1981, 1982, 1983 by Lewis Thomas. "Junius Maltby" from PASTURES OF HEAVEN by John Steinbeck. Copyright 1932, renewed © 1960 by John Steinbeck.

ILLUSTRATION AND PHOTOGRAPHY CREDITS

Steve Moore 6, 10, 13, 18, 22, 27, 31, 32, 116, 124, 130. Susan Gaber 36. Barbara Morgan 38. NASA 40, 43. Marlis Muller 48. Lonny Kalfus 52. Erich Hartmann/Magnum 56. Arthur Tress 58. Wide World Photos 60. Bruce Davidson/Magnum 65. Alex Harris 66, 70. Robert Burroughs 72. Eric Velasquez 74, 79, 82, 87, 92, 94. Darryl Zudeck 98, 102, 104, 138, 140, 143. Jerry Cooke 106. Ken Hamilton 108, 113, 148. Alfred Gescheidt, 123. Bill Basso 134. Newsweek/Lester Sloan 150. Ira Rudolph/Orion 156. Scholastic Photography Awards 160. Suzanne Richardson 164, 170, 177, 182, 190.

CONTENTS

POETRY

DRAMA

"Yes, he's a pleasant little thing, isn't he?

James Herriot
NIGHT OF THE HUNT BALL

● James Herriot's stories of his life as a veterinarian in rural England, in books such as All Things Bright and Beautiful and All Creatures Great and Small, have won him fans worldwide. A compassionate man, he rarely viewed his work as "just a job" but became personally involved with all his patients. He could not always follow his emotions, however, when they conflicted with his professional duties as a doctor.

IT WAS WHEN MY BOSS SIEGFRIED AND I WERE MAKING one of our market day trips to Darrowby, that we noticed the little dog. He was sitting up begging in front of the biscuit stall.

"Look at that little chap," Siegfried said. "I wonder where he's sprung from."

As he spoke, the stallholder threw a biscuit which the dog devoured eagerly. But when the man came round and stretched out a hand, the little animal trotted away.

He stopped, however, at another stall which sold eggs, cheese, butter, and cakes. Without hesitation he sat up again in the begging position, rock-steady, paws dangling, head pointed expectantly.

I nudged Siegfried. "There he goes again."

My colleague nodded. "Yes, he's a pleasant little thing, isn't he? What breed would you call him?"

"A cross, I'd say. He's like a little brown sheepdog, but there's a touch of something else — maybe terrier."

It wasn't long before he was munching a bun. This time we walked over to him. As we drew near I spoke gently.

7

"Here, boy," I said, squatting down a yard away. "Come on, let's have a look at you."

He faced me and, for a moment, two friendly brown eyes gazed at me from an attractive little face. The fringed tail waved in response to my words, but as I inched nearer he turned and ambled unhurriedly among the market crowd till he was lost to sight.

I was standing there when a young policeman came up to me.

"I've been watching that little dog begging among the stalls all morning," he said. "But like you, I haven't been able to get near him."

"Yes, it's strange. He's obviously friendly, yet he's afraid. I wonder who owns him."

"I reckon he's a stray, Mr. Herriot. I'm interested in dogs myself and I think I know just about all of them around here. But this one's a stranger to me."

I nodded. "I bet you're right. So anything could have happened to him. He could have been ill-treated by somebody and run away, or he could have been dumped from a car."

"Yes," he replied. "There are some lovely people around! It beats me how anybody can leave a helpless animal to fend for itself like that. I've had a few tries at catching him myself, but it's no good."

The memory stayed with me for the rest of the day. Even when I lay in bed that night, I was unable to drive away the disturbing image of the little brown creature wandering in a strange world, sitting up asking for help in the only way he knew.

On the Friday night of the same week, Siegfried and I were putting on our evening clothes for the Hunt Ball at East Hirdsley, about ten miles away.

It was a long, drawn-out business because those were the days of starched shirt fronts and stiff high collars. I was in an even worse plight because I had outgrown my suit. Even when I had managed to button the strangling collar, I had to fight my way into the dinner jacket which nipped me cruelly under the arms. I had just managed to put on the complete outfit and was trying out a few careful breaths, when the phone rang.

It was the same young policeman I had been speaking to earlier in the week. "We've got that dog around here, Mr. Herriot. You know — the one that was begging in the marketplace."

"Oh, yes? Somebody's managed to catch him, then?"

There was a pause. "No, not really. One of our men found him lying by the roadside about a mile out of town and brought him in. He's been in an accident."

I told Siegfried. He looked at his watch. "Always happens, doesn't it, James. Just when we're ready to go out. It's nine o'clock now and we should be on our way." He thought for a moment. "Anyway, slip round there and have a look and I'll wait for you. It would be better if we could go to this affair together."

As I drove to the police station, I hoped fervently that there wouldn't be much to do. This Hunt Ball meant a lot to my boss. He would have a wonderful time just chatting and drinking with so many fellow horse lovers, even though he hardly danced at all. Also, he maintained, it was good for his business as a veterinary surgeon to meet his clients socially.

The kennels were at the bottom of a yard behind the Station. The policeman led me down and opened one of the doors. The little dog was lying very still under a single light bulb. When I bent and stroked the brown coat, his tail stirred briefly among the straw of his bed.

"He can still manage a wag anyway," I said.

The policeman nodded. "Aye, there's no doubt he's a good-natured little thing."

I tried to examine him as much as possible without touching. I didn't want to hurt him, and there was no saying what the extent of his injuries might be. But even at a glance, certain things were obvious. He had multiple wounds, one hind leg was fractured, and there was blood on his lips.

This could be from damaged teeth, and I gently raised the head with a view to looking into his mouth. He was lying on his right side. As the head came around it was as though somebody had struck me in the face.

The right eye had been violently dislodged from its socket.

I seemed to squat there for a long time, stunned by the obscenity. As the seconds dragged by, I looked into the little dog's face and he looked back at me — trustingly, from one soft brown eye.

The policeman's voice broke my thoughts. "He's a mess, isn't he?"

"Yes . . . yes . . . must have been struck by some vehicle — maybe dragged along by the look of all those wounds."

"What d'you think, Mr. Herriot?"

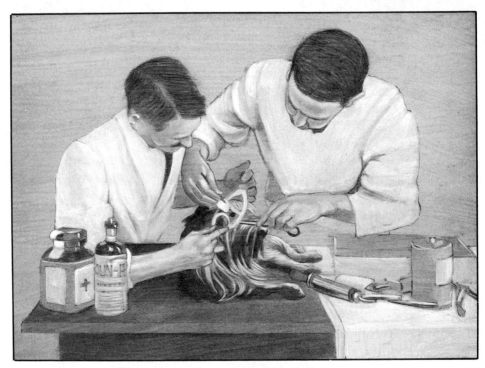

"Oh, forget the Hunt Ball. Let's get busy."

I knew what he meant. It was the sensible thing to ease this lost, unwanted creature from the world. He was grievously hurt, and he didn't seem to belong to anybody. A quick overdose of anesthetic — his troubles would be over and I'd be on my way to the dance.

But the policeman didn't say anything of the sort. Maybe, like me, he was looking into the soft depths of that one trusting eye.

I stood up quickly. "Can I use your phone?"

At the other end of the line Siegfried's voice crackled with impatience. "It's half-past nine, James! If we're going to this thing we've got to go now or we might as well not bother. A stray dog, badly injured. It doesn't sound like such a great problem."

"I know, Siegfried. I'm sorry to hold you up, but I can't make up my mind. I wish you'd come round and tell me what you think."

There was a silence, then a long sigh. "All right, James. See you in five minutes."

He created a slight stir as he entered the Station. Even in his casual working clothes; Siegfried always managed to look distinguished. But as he swept into the Station newly bathed and shaved, a camel coat thrown over the sparkling white shirt and black tie, there was something regal [1] about him.

10

He drew respectful glances from the men sitting around, then my young policeman stepped forward.

"This way, sir," he said, and we went back to the kennels.

Siegfried was silent as he crouched over the dog, looking him over, as I had done, without touching him. Then he carefully raised the head and the monstrous eye glared.

"Good Heavens!" he said softly, and at the sound of his voice the long fringed tail moved along the ground.

For a few seconds Siegfried stayed very still, looking fixedly at the dog's face. In the silence, the whisking tail rustled the straw.

Then he straightened up. "Let's get him round there," he murmured.

In the surgery we anesthetized the little animal. As he lay unconscious on the table we were able to examine him thoroughly. After a few minutes Siegfried stuffed his stethoscope into the pocket of his white coat and leaned both hands on the table.

"Luxated eyeball, fractured thigh bone, umpteen deep wounds, broken claws. There's enough here to keep us going till midnight, James."

I didn't say anything.

My boss pulled the knot from his black tie. He peeled off the stiff collar and hung it on the cross bar of the surgery lamp.

"That's better," he muttered, and began laying out materials to stitch up the wounds.

I looked at him across the table. "How about the Hunt Ball?"

"Oh, forget the Hunt Ball," Siegfried said. "Let's get busy."

We were busy, too, for a long time. I hung up my collar next to my colleague's and we began on the eye. I knew we both felt the same — we wanted to get rid of that horror before we did anything else.

I lubricated the great ball and pulled the eyelids apart while Siegfried gently maneuvered it back into the orbital cavity. I sighed as everything slid out of sight, leaving only the cornea[2] visible.

Siegfried chuckled with satisfaction. "Looks like an eye again, doesn't it?" He seized the ophthalmoscope and peered into the depths.

"And there's no major damage — could be as good as new again. But we'll just stitch the lids together to protect it for a few days."

The broken ends of the fractured leg were badly displaced and we had to struggle to bring them into position before applying the plaster of paris. But at last we finished and started on the long job of stitching the many cuts and wounds.

We worked separately for this, and for a long time it was quiet in the operating room except for the snip of scissors as we clipped the brown hair away from the wounds. I knew and Siegfried knew that we were almost certainly working without payment, but the most disturbing thought was that after all our efforts we might still have to put him asleep. He was still in the care of the police and if nobody claimed him within ten days it meant euthanasia.[3] And if his late owners were really interested in his fate, why hadn't they tried to contact the police before now?

By the time we had completed our work and washed the instruments it was after midnight. Siegfried dropped the last needle into its tray and looked at the sleeping animal.

"I think he's beginning to come round," he said. "Let's take him through to the fire and we can have a drink while he recovers."

We stretchered the dog through to the sitting-room on a blanket and laid him on the rug before the brightly burning coals. With our starched white shirts and braided evening trousers to remind us of the lost dance, we lay back in our chairs on either side of the fireplace. Between us our patient stretched peacefully.

He was a happier sight now. One eye was closed by the protecting stitches and his hind leg projected stiffly in its white cast, but he was tidy, cleaned up, cared for. He looked as though he belonged to somebody — but then there was a great big doubt about that.

It was nearly one o'clock in the morning when the shaggy brown head began to move.

Siegfried leaned forward and touched one of his ears. Immediately the tail flapped against the rug and a pink tongue lazily licked his fingers.

"What an absolutely grand little dog," he murmured, but his voice had a distant quality. I knew he was worried, too.

I took the stitches out of the eyelids in two days and was delighted to find a normal eye underneath.

The young policeman was as pleased as I was. "Look at that!" he exclaimed. "You'd never know anything had happened there."

"Yes, it's done wonderfully well. All the swelling and inflammation has gone." I hesitated for a moment. "Has anybody inquired about him?"

"Looks as though he's been a success.'

He shook his head. "Nothing yet. But there's another eight days to go and we're taking good care of him here."

I visited the Police Station several times and the little animal greeted me with undisguised joy. All his fear was gone. He stood upright against my legs on his plastered limb, his tail swishing.

But all the time my sense of foreboding[4] increased, and on the tenth day I made my way almost with dread to the police kennels. I had heard nothing. My course of action seemed inevitable. Putting old or hopelessly ill dogs to sleep was often an act of mercy, but when it was a young healthy dog it was terrible. I hated it, but it was one of the things veterinary surgeons had to do.

The young policeman was standing in the doorway.

"Still no news?" I asked, and he shook his head.

I went past him into the kennel. The shaggy little creature stood up against my legs as before, laughing into my face, mouth open, eyes shining.

I turned away quickly. I'd have to do this right now or I'd never do it.

"Mr. Herriot." The policeman put his hand on my arm. "I think I'll take him."

"You?" I stared at him.

"Aye, that's right. We get a lot o' stray dogs in here and though I feel sorry for them you can't give them all a home, can you?"

"No, you can't," I said. "I have the same problem."

He nodded slowly. "But somehow this one's different, and it seems to me he's just come at the right time. I have two little girls and they've been at me for a bit to get 'em a dog. This little bloke looks just right for the job."

Warm relief began to ebb through me. "I couldn't agree more. He's the soul of good nature. I bet he'll be wonderful with children."

"Good. That's settled then. I thought I'd ask your advice first." He smiled happily.

I looked at him as though I had never seen him before. "What's your name?"

"Phelps," he replied. "P.C. Phelps."

He was a good-looking young fellow, clean-skinned, with cheerful blue eyes and a solid, dependable look about him. I had to fight against an impulse to shake his hand and thump him on the back. But I managed to preserve the professional exterior.

"Well, that's fine." I bent and stroked the little dog. "Don't forget to bring him along to the surgery in ten days for removal of the stitches, and we'll have to get that plaster off in about a month."

It was Siegfried who took out the stitches, and I didn't see our patient again until four weeks later.

P.C. Phelps had his little girls, aged four and six, with him, as well as the dog.

"You said the plaster ought to come off about now," he said, and I nodded.

He looked down at the children. "Well, come on, you two, lift him on the table."

Eagerly the little girls put their arms around their new pet, and as they hoisted him the tail wagged furiously and the wide mouth panted in delight.

"Looks as though he's been a success," I said.

He smiled. "That's an understatement. He's perfect with those two. I can't tell you what pleasure he's given us. He's one of the family."

I got out my little saw and began to hack at the plaster.

"It's worked both ways, I should say. A dog loves a secure home."

"Well, he couldn't be more secure." He ran his hand along the brown coat and laughed as he addressed the little dog. "That's what you get for begging among the stalls on market day, my lad. You're in the hands of the law now."

[1] **regal:** royal
[2] **cornea:** the transparent part of the outer coat of the eyeball
[3] **euthanasia:** mercy killing
[4] **foreboding:** feeling that something bad is about to happen

A CLOSER LOOK

1. Why does Herriot miss the Hunt Ball? How does he feel about this? How does his boss, Siegfried, feel about it?

2. What qualities in the dog appeal to Herriot? What does this tell you about his own set of values?

3. Would you call Herriot a sentimental man? Support your opinion with evidence from the story.

● Like an old folk song, this poem asks a series of riddles, then gives its own answers. Look for what all the answers have in common — Silverstein has a definite statement to make.

Shel Silverstein

HOW MANY, HOW MUCH

How many slams in an old screen door?
Depends how loud you shut it.
How many slices in a bread?
Depends how thin you cut it.
How much good inside a day?
Depends how good you live 'em.
How much love inside a friend?
Depends how much you give 'em.

• Each short line of this poem is dense with willpower and fierce determination. Is it a poem of hope or a poem of despair? Read it several times — it may be both.

Mari Evans

THE SILVER CELL

I have
never been contained
except I
made
the prison, nor
known a chain
except those forged
by me

O I am slave
and I am master
am at once
both bound
and free

"The best four years of your whole life are just about to begin."

Kurt Vonnegut

THE LIE

● Although best known for his comic science fiction, Kurt Vonnegut is very much concerned about how we live our lives today on Earth. This story deals with parental pressures, and with the problems created by parents who try to turn a child into something he is not.

T WAS EARLY SPRINGTIME. WEAK SUNSHINE LAY cold on old gray frost. Willow twigs against the sky showed the golden haze of fat catkins about to bloom. A black Rolls-Royce streaked up the Connecticut Turnpike from New York City. At the wheel was Ben Barkley, the chauffeur.

"Keep it under the speed limit, Ben," said Doctor Remenzel. "I don't care how ridiculous any speed limit seems, stay under it. No reason to rush — we have plenty of time."

Ben eased off on the throttle. "Seems like in the springtime she wants to get up and go," he said.

"Do what you can to keep her down — OK?" said the doctor.

"Yes, sir!" said Ben. He spoke in a lower voice to the thirteen-year-old boy who was riding beside him, to Eli Remenzel, the doctor's son. "Ain't just people and animals feel good in the springtime," he said to Eli. "Motors feel good, too."

"Um," said Eli.

"Everything feels good," said Ben. "Don't you feel good?"

"Sure, sure I feel good," said Eli emptily.

"Should feel good — going to that wonderful school," said Ben.

That wonderful school was the Whitehill School for Boys, a private preparatory school in North Marston, Massachusetts. That was where the Rolls-Royce was bound. The plan was that Eli would enroll for the fall semester, while his father, a member of the class of 1939, attended a meeting of the Board of Overseers of the school.

"Don't believe this boy's feeling so good, Doctor," said Ben. He wasn't particularly serious about it. It was more genial[1] springtime blather.[2]

"What's the matter, Eli?" said the doctor absently. He was studying blueprints, plans for a thirty-room addition to the Eli Remenzel Memorial Dormitory — a building named in honor of his great-great-grandfather. Doctor Remenzel had the plans draped over a walnut table that folded out of the back of the front seat. He was a massive, dignified man, a physician, a healer for healing's sake, since he had been born as rich as the Shah of Iran. "Worried about something?" he asked Eli without looking up from the plans.

"Nope," said Eli.

"Eli's lovely mother, Sylvia, sat next to the doctor, reading the catalogue of the Whitehill School. "If I were you," she said to Eli, "I'd be so excited I could hardly stand it. The best four years of your whole life are just about to begin."

"Sure," said Eli. He didn't show her his face. He gave her only the back of his head, a pinwheel of coarse brown hair above a stiff white collar, to talk to.

"I wonder how many Remenzels have gone to Whitehill," said Sylvia.

"That's like asking how many people are dead in a cemetery," said the doctor. He gave the answer to the old joke, and to Sylvia's question, too. "All of 'em."

The question annoyed Doctor Remenzel a little. It didn't seem in very good taste. "It isn't the sort of thing you keep score on," he said.

"Guess," said his wife.

"Oh," he said, "you'd have to go back through all the records, all the way back to the end of the eighteenth century, even, to make any kind of a guess. And you'd have to decide whether to count the Schofields and the Haleys and the MacLellans as Remenzels."

"Please make a guess — " said Sylvia, "just people whose last names were Remenzel."

"Oh — " The doctor shrugged, rattled the plans."Thirty maybe."

"So Eli is number thirty-one!" said Sylvia, delighted with the number. "You're number thirty-one, dear," she said to the back of Eli's head.

Doctor Remenzel rattled the plans again. "I don't want him going around saying something asinine,[3] like he's number thirty-one," he said.

"Eli knows better than that," said Sylvia. She was a game, ambitious woman, with no money of her own at all. She had been married for sixteen years, but was still openly curious and enthusiastic about the ways of families that had been rich for many generations.

"Just for my own curiosity — not so Eli can go around saying what number he is," said Sylvia, "I'm going to go wherever they keep the records and find out what number he is. That's what I'll do while you're at the meeting and Eli's doing whatever he has to do at the Admissions Office."

"All right," said Doctor Remenzel, "you go ahead and *do* that."

"I will," said Sylvia. "I think things like that are interesting, even if you don't." She waited for a rise on that, but didn't get one. Sylvia enjoyed arguing with her husband about her lack of reserve and his excess of it. She enjoyed saying, toward the end of arguments like that, "Well, I guess I'm just a simple-minded country girl at heart, and that's all I'll ever be, and I'm afraid you're going to have to get used to it."

But Doctor Remenzel didn't want to play that game. He found the dormitory plans more interesting.

"Will the new rooms have fireplaces?" said Sylvia. In the oldest part of the dormitory, several of the rooms had handsome fireplaces.

"That would practically double the cost of construction," said the doctor.

"I want Eli to have a room with a fireplace, if that's possible," said Sylvia.

"Those rooms are for seniors."

"I thought maybe through some fluke — " said Sylvia.

"What kind of fluke do you have in mind?" said the doctor. "You mean I should demand that Eli be given a room with a fireplace?"

"Not *demand* — " said Sylvia.

"Request firmly?" said the doctor.

21

"The Rolls-Royce pulled abreast of an old Chevrolet."

"Maybe I'm just a simple-minded country girl at heart," said Sylvia, "but I look through this catalogue, and I see all the buildings named after Remenzels. I look through the back and see all the hundreds of thousands of dollars given by Remenzels for scholarships, and I just can't help thinking people named Remenzel are entitled to ask for a little something extra."

"Let me tell you in no uncertain terms," said Doctor Remenzel, "that you are not to ask for anything special for Eli — not anything."

"Of course I won't," said Sylvia. "Why do you always think I'm going to embarrass you?"

"I don't," he said.

"But I can still think what I think, can't I?" she said.

"If you have to," he said.

"I have to," she said cheerfully, utterly unrepentant.[4] She leaned over the plans. "You think those people will like those rooms?"

"What people?" he said.

"The Africans," she said. She was talking about thirty Africans who, at the request of the State Department, were being admitted to Whitehill in the coming semester. It was because of them that the

22

dormitory was being expanded.

"The rooms aren't for them," he said. "They aren't going to be segregated."

"Oh," said Sylvia. She thought about this awhile, and then she said, "Is there a chance Eli will have to have one of them for a roommate?"

"Freshmen draw lots for roommates," said the doctor. "That piece of information's in the catalogue, too."

"Eli?" said Sylvia.

"H'm?" said Eli.

"How would you feel about it if you had to room with one of those Africans?"

Eli shrugged listlessly.[5]

"That's all right?" said Sylvia.

Eli shrugged again.

"I guess it's all right," said Sylvia.

"It had better be," said the doctor.

The Rolls-Royce pulled abreast of an old Chevrolet, a car in such bad repair that its back door was lashed shut with clothesline. Doctor Remenzel glanced casually at the driver, and then, with sudden excitement and pleasure, he told Ben Barkley to stay abreast of the car.

The doctor leaned across Sylvia, rolled down his window, and yelled to the driver of the old Chevrolet, "Tom! Tom!"

The man was a Whitehill classmate of the doctor. He wore a Whitehill necktie, which he waved at Doctor Remenzel in gay recognition. And then he pointed to the fine young son who sat beside him. He conveyed with proud smiles and nods that the boy was bound for Whitehill.

Doctor Remenzel pointed to the chaos of the back of Eli's head, beamed that his news was the same. In the wind blustering between the two cars they made a lunch date at the Holly House in North Marston, at the inn whose principal business was serving visitors to Whitehill.

"All right," said Doctor Remenzel to Ben Barkley, "drive on."

"You know," said Sylvia, "somebody really ought to write an article — " And she turned to look through the back window at the old car now shuddering far behind. "Somebody really ought to."

"What about?" said the doctor. He noticed that Eli had slumped way down in the front seat. "Eli!" he said sharply. "Sit up straight!'' He returned his attention to Sylvia.

"Most people think prep schools are such snobbish things, just for people with money," said Sylvia, "but that isn't true." She leafed through the catalogue and found the quotation she was after.

"The Whitehill School operates on the assumption," she read, *"that no boy should be deterred[6] from applying for admission because his family is unable to pay the full cost of a Whitehill education. With this in mind, the Admissions Committee selects each year from approximately 3000 candidates the 150 most promising and deserving boys, regardless of their parents' ability to pay the full $2200 tuition. And those in need of financial aid are given it to the full extent of their need. In certain instances, the school will even pay for the clothing and transportation of a boy."*

Sylvia shook her head. "I think that's perfectly amazing. It's something most people don't realize at all. A truckdriver's son can come to Whitehill."

"If he's smart enough," he said.

"Thanks to the Remenzels," said Sylvia with pride.

"And a lot of other people, too," said the doctor.

Sylvia read out loud again: *"In 1799, Eli Remenzel laid the foundation for the present Scholarship Fund by donating to the school forty acres in Boston. The school still owns twelve of those acres. Their current evaluation bring $3,000,000."*

"Eli!" said the doctor. "Sit up! What's the matter with you?"

Eli sat up again, but began to slump almost immediately. He had good reason for slumping, for actually hoping to die or disappear. He could not bring himself to say what the reason was. He slumped because he knew he had been denied admission to Whitehill. He had failed the entrance examinations. Eli's parents did not know this, because Eli had found the awful notice in the mail and had torn it up.

Doctor Remenzel and his wife had no doubts whatsoever about their son's getting into Whitehill. It was inconceivable to them that Eli could not go there, so they had no curiosity as to how Eli had done on the examination, were not puzzled when no report ever came.

"What all will Eli have to do to enroll?" said Sylvia, as the black Rolls-Royce crossed the Rhode Island border.

"I don't know," said the doctor. "I suppose they've got it all complicated now with forms to be filled out in quadruplicate, and punch-card machines and bureaucrats.[7] This business of entrance examinations is all new, too. In my day a boy simply had an interview with the headmaster. The headmaster would look him over, ask him a few questions, and then say, 'There's a Whitehill boy.' ''

"Did he ever say, 'There isn't a Whitehill boy?' " said Sylvia.

"Oh, sure," said Doctor Remenzel, "if a boy was impossibly stupid or something. There have to be standards. There have always been standards. The African boys have to meet the standards, just like anybody else. They aren't getting in just because the State Department wants to make friends. We made that clear. Those boys had to meet the standards."

"And they did?" said Sylvia.

"I suppose," said Doctor Remenzel. "I heard they're all in, and they all took the examination Eli did."

"Was it a hard examination, dear?" Sylvia asked Eli. It was the first time she'd thought to ask.

"Um," said Eli.

"What?" she said.

"Yes," said Eli.

"I'm glad they've got high standards," she said, and then she realized that this was a fairly silly statement. "Of course they've got high standards," she said. "That's why it's such a famous school. That's why people who go there do so well in later life."

Sylvia resumed her reading of the catalogue and opened out a folding map of "The Sward," as the campus of Whitehill was traditionally called. She read off the names of features that memorialized Remenzels — the Sanford Remenzel Bird Sanctuary, the George MacLellan Remenzel Skating Rink, the Eli Remenzel Memorial Dormitory, and then she read out loud a quatrain printed on one corner of the map:

> "When night falleth gently
> Upon the green Sward,
> It's Whitehill, dear Whitehill,
> "Our thoughts all turn toward."

"You know," said Sylvia, "school songs are so corny when you just read them. But when I hear the Glee Club sing those words, they sound like the most beautiful words ever written, and I want to cry.''

"Um," said Doctor Remenzel.

"Did a Remenzel write them?''

"I don't think so," said Doctor Remenzel. And then he said, "No — Wait. That's the *new* song. A Remenzel didn't write it. Tom Kilyer wrote it."

"The man in that old car we passed?''

"Sure," said Doctor Remenzel. "Tom wrote it. I remember when he wrote it."

"A scholarship boy wrote it?" said Sylvia. "I think that's awfully nice. He *was* a scholarship boy, wasn't he?''

"His father was an ordinary automobile mechanic in North Marston.''

"You hear what a democratic school you're going to, Eli?" said Sylvia.

Half an hour later Ben Barkley brought the limousine to a stop before the Holly House, a rambling country inn twenty years older than the Republic. The inn was on the edge of the Whitehill Sward.

Ben Barkley was sent away with the car for an hour and a half. Doctor Remenzel shepherded[8] Sylvia and Eli into a familiar, low-ceilinged world of pewter, clocks, lovely old woods, agreeable servants, elegant food, and drink.

Eli, clumsy with horror of what was surely to come, banged a grandmother clock with his elbow as he passed, and made the clock cry.

Sylvia excused herself. Doctor Remenzel and Eli went to the threshold[9] of the dining room, where a hostess welcomed them both by name. They were given a table beneath an oil portrait of one of three Whitehill boys who had gone on to become president of the United States.

The dining room was filling quickly with families. What every family had was at least one boy about Eli's age. Most of the boys wore Whitehill blazers — black, with pale-blue piping, with Whitehill seals on their breast pockets. A few, like Eli, were not yet entitled to wear blazers. They were simply hoping to get in.

The doctor ordered a martini, then turned to his son and said, "Your mother has the idea that you're entitled to special privileges around here. I hope you don't have that idea, too.''

"How fast things change these days!"

"No, sir," said Eli.

"It would be a source of the greatest embarrassment to me," said Doctor Remenzel with considerable grandeur, "if I were ever to hear that you had used the name Remenzel as though you thought Remenzels were something special."

"I know," said Eli wretchedly.

"That settles it," said the doctor. He had nothing more to say about it. He gave abbreviated salutes to several people he knew in the room, speculated[10] as to what sort of party had reserved a long banquet table that was set up along one wall. He decided that it was for a visiting athletic team. Sylvia arrived, and Eli had to be told in a sharp whisper to stand when a woman came to a table.

Sylvia was full of news. The long table, she related, was for the thirty boys from Africa. "I'll bet that's more black people than have eaten here since this place was founded," she said softly. "How fast things change these days!"

"You're right about how fast things change," said Doctor Remenzel. "You're wrong about the black people who've eaten here. This used to be a busy part of the Underground Railroad."[11]

"Really?" said Sylvia. "How exciting." She looked all about

27

herself in a birdlike way. "I think everything's exciting here. I only wish Eli had a blazer on."

Doctor Remenzel reddened. "He isn't entitled to one," he said.

"I know that," said Sylvia.

"I thought you were going to ask somebody for permission to put a blazer on Eli right away," said the doctor.

"I wouldn't do that," said Sylvia, a little offended now. "Why are you always afraid I'll embarrass you?"

"Never mind. Excuse me. Forget it," said Doctor Remenzel.

Sylvia brightened again, put her hand on Eli's arm, and looked radiantly at a man in the dining-room doorway. "There's my favorite person in all the world, next to my son and husband," she said. She meant Dr. Donald Warren, headmaster of the Whitehill School. A thin gentleman in his early sixties, Doctor Warren was in the doorway with the manager of the inn, looking over the arrangements for the Africans.

It was then that Eli got up abruptly, fled the dining room, fled as much of the nightmare as he could possibly leave behind. He brushed past Doctor Warren rudely, even though he knew him well, and Doctor Warren spoke his name. Doctor Warren looked after him sadly.

"I'll be darned," said Doctor Remenzel. "What brought that on?"

"Maybe he really *is* sick," said Sylvia.

The Remenzels had no time to react more elaborately, because Doctor Warren spotted them and crossed quickly to their table. When he greeted them, some of his perplexity[12] about Eli showed in his greeting. He asked if he might sit down.

"Certainly, of course," said Doctor Remenzel expansively.[13] "We'd be honored if you did."

"Not to eat," said Doctor Warren. "I'll be eating at the long table with the new boys. I would like to talk, though." He saw that there were five places set at the table. "You're expecting someone?"

"We passed Tom Hilyer and his boy on the way," said Doctor Remenzel. "They'll be along in a minute."

"Good, good," said Doctor Warren absently. He fidgeted and looked again in the direction in which Eli had disappeared.

"Tom's boy will be going to Whitehill in the fall?" said Doctor Remenzel.

"H'm?" said Doctor Warren. "Oh — yes, yes. Yes, he will."

"Is he a scholarship boy, like his father?" said Sylvia.

"That's not a polite question," said Doctor Remenzel severely.

"I beg your pardon," said Sylvia.

"No, no — that's a perfectly proper question these days," said Doctor Warren. "We don't keep that sort of information very secret anymore. We're proud of our scholarship boys, and they have every reason to be proud of themselves. Tom's boy got the highest score anyone's ever got on the entrance examinations. We feel privileged to have him."

"We never *did* find out Eli's score," said Doctor Remenzel. He said it with good-humored resignation.[14] He did not expect that Eli had done especially well.

"A good strong medium, I imagine," said Sylvia. She said this on the basis of Eli's grades in primary school, which had ranged from medium to terrible.

The headmaster looked surprised. "I didn't tell you his scores?" he said.

"We haven't seen you since he took the examinations," said Doctor Remenzel.

"The letter I wrote you — " said Doctor Warren.

"What letter?" said Doctor Remenzel. "Did we get a letter?"

"A letter from me," said Doctor Warren, with growing incredulity.[15] "The hardest letter I ever had to write."

Sylvia shook her head. "We never got any letter from you."

Doctor Warren sat back, looking very ill. "I mailed it myself," he said. "It was definitely mailed — two weeks ago."

Doctor Remenzel shrugged. "The U.S. mails don't lose much," he said, "but I guess that now and then something gets misplaced."

Doctor Warren cradled his head in his hands. "Oh, dear — oh, my," he said. "I was surprised to see Eli here. I wondered that he would want to come along with you."

"He didn't come along just to see the scenery," said Doctor Remenzel. "He came to enroll."

"I want to know what was in the letter," said Sylvia.

Doctor Warren raised his head and folded his hands. "What the letter said was this, and no other words could be more difficult for me to say: *'On the basis of his work in primary school and his scores on the entrance examinations, I must tell you that your son and my good friend Eli cannot possibly do the work required of boys at Whitehill.' "* Doctor Warren's voice steadied, and so did his gaze. " *'To admit Eli to Whitehill, to expect him to do Whitehill work,' "* he said, " *'would be both unrealistic and cruel.' "*

Thirty African boys, escorted by several faculty members, State Department men, and diplomats from their own countries, filed into the dining room.

And Tom Hilyer and his boy, having no idea that something had just gone awfully wrong for the Remenzels, came in, too, and said hello to the Remenzels and Doctor Warren gaily, as though life couldn't possibly be better.

"I'll talk to you more about this later if you like," Doctor Warren said to the Remenzels, rising. "I have to go now, but later on — " He left quickly.

"My mind's a blank," said Sylvia. "My mind's a perfect blank."

Tom Hilyer and his boy sat down. Hilyer looked at the menu before him, clapped his hands, and said, "What's good? I'm hungry." And then he said, "Say — where's your boy?"

"He stepped out for a moment," said Doctor Remenzel evenly.

"We've got to find him," said Sylvia to her husband.

"In time, in due time," said Doctor Remenzel.

"That letter," said Sylvia; "Eli knew about it. He found it and tore it up. Of course he did!" She started to cry, thinking of the hideous trap that Eli had caught himself in.

"I'm not interested right now in what Eli's done," said Doctor Remenzel. "Right now I'm a lot more interested in what some other people are going to do."

"What do you mean?" said Sylvia.

"Doctor Remenzel stood impressively, angry and determined. "I mean," he said, "I'm going to see how quickly people can change their minds around here."

"Please," said Sylvia, trying to hold him, trying to calm him, "we've got to find Eli. That's the first thing."

"The first thing," said Doctor Remenzel quite loudly, "is to get Eli admitted to Whitehill. After that we'll find him, and we'll bring him back."

"But darling — " said Sylvia.

"No but about it," said Doctor Remenzel. "There's a majority of the Board of Overseers in this room at this very moment. Every one of them is a close friend of mine, or a close friend of my father. If

The Whitehill School

they tell Doctor Warren Eli's in, that's it — Eli's in. If there's room for all these other people," he said, "there's room for Eli, too."

He strode quickly to a table nearby, sat down heavily, and began to talk to a fierce-looking and splendid old gentleman who was eating there. The old gentleman was chairman of the board.

Sylvia apologized to the baffled Hilyers, and then went in search of Eli.

Asking this person and that person, Sylvia found him. He was outside — all alone on a bench in a bower of lilacs that had just begun to bud.

Eli heard his mother's coming on the gravel path, and stayed where he was, resigned. "Did you find out," he said, "or do I still have to tell you?"

"About you?" she said gently. "About not getting in? Doctor Warren told us."

"I tore his letter up," said Eli.

"I can understand that," she said. "Your father and I have always made you feel that you had to go to Whitehill, that nothing else would do."

"I feel better," said Eli. He tried to smile, found he could do it

31

"Did you find out, or do I still have to tell you?"

easily. "I feel so much better now that it's over. I tried to tell you a couple of times — but I just couldn't. I didn't know how."

"That's my fault, not yours," she said.

"What's father doing?" said Eli.

Sylvia was so intent on comforting Eli that she'd put out of her mind what her husband was up to. Now she realized that Doctor Remenzel was making a ghastly mistake. She didn't want Eli admitted to Whitehill. She could see what a cruel thing that would be.

She couldn't bring herself to tell the boy what his father was doing, so she said, "He'll be along in a minute, dear. He understands." And then she said, "You wait here, and I'll go get him and come right back."

But she didn't have to go to Doctor Remenzel. At that moment the big man came out of the inn and caught sight of his wife and son. He came to her and to Eli. He looked dazed.

"Well?" she said.

"They — they all said no," said Doctor Remenzel, very subdued.[16]

"That's for the best," said Sylvia. "I'm relieved. I really am."

32

"Who said no?" said Eli. "Who said no to what?"

"The members of the board," said Doctor Remenzel, not looking anyone in the eye. "I asked them to make an exception in your case — to reverse their decision and let you in."

Eli stood, his face filled with incredulity and shame that were instant. "You what?" he said, and there was no childishness in the way he said it. Next came anger. "You shouldn't have done that!" he said to his father.

Doctor Remenzel nodded. "So I've already been told."

"That isn't done!" said Eli. "How awful! You shouldn't have."

"You're right," said Doctor Remenzel, accepting the scolding lamely.

"Now I *am* ashamed," said Eli, and he showed that he was.

Doctor Remenzel, in his wretchedness, could find no strong words to say. "I apologize to you both," he said at last. "It was a very bad thing to try."

"Now a Remenzel *has* asked for something," said Eli.

"I don't suppose Ben's back yet with the car?" said Doctor Remenzel. It was obvious that Ben wasn't. "We'll wait out here for him," he said. "I don't want to go back in there now."

"A Remenzel asked for something — as though a Remenzel were something special," said Eli.

"I don't suppose — " said Doctor Remenzel, and he left the sentence unfinished, dangling in the air.

"You don't suppose what?" said his wife, her face puzzled.

"I don't suppose," said Doctor Remenzel, "that we'll ever be coming here any more."

---

[1] **genial:** kindly, friendly
[2] **blather:** chatter; foolish talk
[3] **asinine:** stupid
[4] **unrepentant:** without feelings of regret
[5] **listlessly:** weakly; without much feeling or force
[6] **deterred:** prevented; turned aside
[7] **bureaucrats:** government officials
[8] **shepherded:** led, as a shepherd leads his flock
[9] **threshold:** door; beginning

[10] **speculated:** guessed; thought about
[11] **Underground Railroad:** a system by which runaway slaves were secretly helped to reach the North
[12] **perplexity:** confusion
[13] **expansively:** with high spirits often accompanied by a sense of self-importance
[14] **resignation:** acceptance of what can't be changed
[15] **incredulity:** disbelief
[16] **subdued:** curbed; brought under control

A CLOSER LOOK

1. During the car trip, what does Eli know that his parents don't know? How does this affect how he feels about their conversation?

2. What does Whitehall School represent to Doctor Remenzel? What does it represent to his wife Sylvia? What does it mean to Eli?

3. Do you think Eli should have been admitted to the school? Would you call him a failure? Why or why not?

Lewis Thomas

THE LIE DETECTOR

● Trained as a biologist, Lewis Thomas likes to examine the scientific phenomena that go on all around us, particularly those that affect us in our daily lives. He isn't just a scientist, however; he asks himself not only "how" but also "why" nature acts in certain ways. Thomas seeks to find the order of the universe within each tiny cell and organism, and to learn lessons about life from biology itself.

HAVE BEEN READING MAGAZINE STORIES ABOUT LIE detectors lately, and it occurs to me that this may be the good news I've been looking for. As I understand it, a human being cannot tell a lie, even a small one, without setting off a kind of smoke alarm somewhere deep in the brain. This results in the sudden discharge of nerve impulses, or neurohormones, or both. The outcome, recorded by the lie-detector, is a cascade[1] of changes in the electrical conductivity of the skin, the heart rate, and the manner of breathing. These responses are similar to the responses which the brain makes to various kinds of stress.

Lying, then, is stressful, even when we do it for protection, or relief, or escape, or profit, or just for the pure pleasure of lying and getting away with it. Lying is a strain that is distressing enough to cause the emission of signals to and from the central nervous system, warning that something has gone wrong. It is, in a pure physiological[2] sense, an unnatural act.

Now I regard this as a piece of extraordinary good news, for it means that we are a moral species by necessity, at least in the sense that we are biologically designed to be truthful to each other. Lying

"Lying is . . . an unnatural act."

that we are biologically designed to be truthful to each other. Lying doesn't hurt, mind you. Perhaps you could tell lies all day and night for years on end without being damaged. But maybe not — maybe the lie detector is informing us that repeated, habitual untruthfulness will gradually damage the sweat glands, the adrenal glands, and who knows what else. Perhaps we should be looking into the possibility that lying is the cause of some of the common human ailments still beyond explaining, such as frequent head colds and a sudden pain in the lower mid-back.

Our inclination to tell the truth may be a biological trait built into our genes. It may be a feature of humanity as characteristic for us as feathers for birds or scales for fish. It may enable us to live, at our best, the kinds of lives we are designed to live.

The alternative explanation is that we are brought up to love the truth as children, in response to the rules of our culture. But if this is the case, you would expect to encounter, every once in a while, societies in which the rule doesn't hold, and I have never heard of a culture in which lying was done by everyone, all life through; nor can I imagine such a group functioning successfully.

Biologically speaking, there is good reason for us to restrain ourselves from lying to each other whenever possible. We are a social species, more interdependent than the social insects. We can no more live a solitary life than can a bee. We are obliged, as a species, to rely on each other. Trust is a fundamental requirement for our kind of existence. Without it all our linkages would begin to snap loose.

The restraint against lying is a mild one, so gentle that we can hardly perceive it. But it is there. We know about it from what we call guilt, and now we have a neat machine to record it as well.

[1] **cascade:** literally, a small waterfall
[2] **physiological:** relating to all the functions of a living organism

A CLOSER LOOK

1. Why does Thomas conclude that lying is stressful?

2. Why does Thomas believe that human beings are moral?

3. Why does Thomas say that trust is a basic requirement for human existence?

● In these joyful verses, Teasdale lists some of her favorite things, each a flash of remembered delight. Her poem, however, is not merely a celebration of life — it is also a code for how to live.

Sara Teasdale

BARTER

Life has loveliness to sell,
  All beautiful and splendid things,
Blue waves whitened on a cliff,
  Soaring fire that sways and sings,
And children's faces looking up
Holding wonder like a cup.

Life has loveliness to sell,
  Music like a curve of gold,
Scent of pine trees in the rain,
  Eyes that love you, arms that hold,
And for your spirit's still delight,
Holy thoughts that star the night.

Spend all you have for loveliness,
  Buy it and never count the cost;
For one white singing hour of peace
  Count many a year of strife well lost,
And for a breath of ecstasy
Give all you have been, or could be.

"Know your planet."

Carl Sagan

TWELVE THINGS I WISH THEY TAUGHT AT SCHOOL

● Carl Sagan no doubt did well in school — he ended up as a professor of astronomy, an advisor to the U.S. space program, and author of a best-selling book and popular TV show, both called Cosmos. His love of knowledge and his excitement about new issues have opened many people's minds to new ways of thinking. Sagan's experiences taught him, however, that facts aren't all that should be taught at school. In this essay, Sagan presents a list of skills and experiences that he believes should be part of everyone's education.

I ATTENDED JUNIOR AND SENIOR HIGH SCHOOL, PUBLIC institutions in New York and New Jersey, just after the Second World War. It seems a long time ago. The facilities and the skills of the teachers were probably well above average for the United States at that time. Since then, I've learned a great deal. One of the most important things I've learned is how much there is to learn, and how much I don't yet know. Sometimes I think how grateful I would be today if I had learned more back then about what really matters. In some respects that education was terribly narrow; the only thing I ever heard in school about Napoleon was that the United States made the Louisiana Purchase from him. (On a planet where some 95% of the inhabitants are not Americans, the only history that was thought worth teaching was American history.) In spelling, grammar, the fundamentals of arithmetic, and other vital subjects, my teachers did a pretty good job. But there's so much else I wish they'd taught us.

Perhaps all the deficiencies[1] I remember have since been rectified.[2] Still, it seems to me there are many things (often more a matter of attitude and perception than the simple memorization of facts) that the schools should teach — things that truly would be useful in later life, useful in making a stronger country and a better world, but useful also in making people happier. Human beings enjoy learning. That's one of the few things that we do better than the other species on our planet. Every student should regularly experience the "Aha!" — when something you never understood, or something you never knew was a mystery, becomes clear.

So here's my list:

● **Pick a difficult thing and learn it well.** The Greek philosopher Socrates said this was one of the greatest of human joys, and it is. While you learn a little bit about many subjects, make sure you learn a great deal about one or two. It hardly matters what the subject is, as long as it deeply interests you, and you place it in its broader human context. After you teach yourself one subject, you become much more confident about your ability to teach yourself another. You gradually find you've acquired a key skill. The world is changing so rapidly that you must continue to teach yourself throughout your life. But don't get trapped by the first subject that interests you, or the first thing you find yourself good at. The world is full of wonders, and some of them we don't discover until we're all grown up. Most of them, sadly, we never discover.

● **Don't be afraid to ask "dumb" questions.** Many apparently naive inquiries — like why grass is green, or why the Sun is round, or why we need 55,000 nuclear weapons in the world — are really deep questions. The answers can be a gateway to real insights. It's also important to know, as well as you can, what it is that you don't know, and asking questions is the way. To ask "dumb" questions requires courage on the part of the asker and knowledge and patience on the part of the answerer. And don't confine your learning to schoolwork. Discuss ideas in depth with friends. It's much braver to ask questions even when there's a prospect of ridicule than to suppress your questions and become deadened to the world around you.

● **Listen carefully.** Many conversations are a kind of competition that rarely leads to discovery on either side. When people are talking, don't spend the time thinking about what you're going to say next. Instead, try to understand what they're saying, what experience informs their remarks, what you can learn from or about

" It's the only planet we have."

them. Older people have grown up in a world very different from yours, one you may not know very well. They, and people from other parts of the country and from other nations, have important perspectives[3] that can enrich your life.

- **Everybody makes mistakes.** Everybody's understanding is incomplete. Be open to correction, and learn to correct your own mistakes. The only embarrassment is in not learning from your mistakes. (Governments almost never admit mistakes. What can we learn from this fact?)

- **Baloney detection.** Fallacies[4] in argumentation are everywhere: in the schools, in the mass media, in the pronouncements of our and other governments. Sometimes the error is unconscious. Other times, it's intentional. For example, a personal attack on someone is not a criticism of his or her argument. This is one of about a dozen common errors of logic and rhetoric.[5] It's called *ad hominem* ("to the man," instead of "to the issue"). Learn these categories of error. Together, they're a baloney detection kit. They have names like "straw man,"[6] "excluded middle,"[7] "*non sequitur*,"[8] and even *"post hoc ergo propter hoc."*[9] A baloney detector helps tell us when we're being lied to. If you're after the truth, it's usually a good thing to separate out the baloney first. (High school algebra and Euclidian geometry, incidentally, provide important insights into what constitutes compelling evidence.)

● **Know your planet.** It's the only one we have. Learn how it works. We're changing the atmosphere, the surface, the waters of the Earth, often for some short-term advantage when the long-term implications are unknown. Especially in a democracy, the citizens should have at least something to say about the direction in which we're going. If we don't understand the issues, we abandon the future.

● **Science and technology.** You can't know your planet unless you know something about science and technology. School science courses, I remember, concentrated on the trivia of science, leaving the major insights almost untouched. The great discoveries in modern science are also great discoveries of the human spirit. For example, Copernicus showed that — far from the Earth being the center of the universe, about which the Sun, the Moon, the planets and the stars revolved in clockwork homage[10] — the Earth is just one of many small worlds. This is a deflation[11] of our pretensions, to be sure, but it is also the opening up to our view of a vast and awesome universe. Every high school graduate should have some notion of the insights of Copernicus, Newton, Darwin, Freud, and Einstein. (Einstein's special theory of relativity, far from being obscure and exceptionally difficult, can be understood in its basics with no more than first-year algebra, and the notion of a rowboat in a river going upstream and downstream.)

● **Nuclear war.** This is the most immediate and most dangerous threat to our species and our world. Learn enough about nuclear weapons, their delivery systems, and nuclear strategy to be able to enter intelligently into what promises to be a continuing worldwide debate, and to work to resolve the growing crisis. If you can make a contribution to this subject, you will have done something for all generations that are and ever will be.

● **Don't spend your life watching TV.** You know what I'm talking about.

● **Culture.** Gain some exposure to the great works of literature, art and music. If such a work is hundreds or thousands of years old and is still admired, there is probably something to it. Like all deep experiences, it may take a little work on your part to discover what all the fuss is about. But once you make the effort, your life has changed; you've acquired a source of enjoyment and excitement for the rest of your days. In a world as tightly connected as ours is, don't restrict your attention to American or Western culture. Learn how and what people elsewhere think. Learn something of their history, their religions, their viewpoints.

● **Politics.** A basic tenet[12] of American democracy, and one of the principles on which the nation was founded, is the protection and encouragement of unpopular beliefs. (Think again about Copernicus.) No nation, sect, or political party has a monopoly on the truth. So consider unpopular views and see if any of them make sense to you. Why, exactly, are they unpopular? Are there deficiencies in the conventional wisdom? Learn something about practical politics. Involve yourself in a local political campaign. Understand how political power is used. There are many evils — chattel[13] slavery, say, or smallpox — that were overcome worldwide, through the combination of new insights and political power. Understanding these advances can help us to deal with other evils in our time.

● **Compassion.** Many people believe that we live in an extraordinarily selfish time. But there is a hollowness, a loneliness that comes from living only for yourself. Humans are capable of great mutual compassion, love, and tenderness. These feelings, however, need encouragement to grow.

Look at the delight a one- or two-year-old takes in learning, and you see how powerful is the human will to learn. Our passion to understand the universe and our compassion for others jointly provide the chief hope of the human species.

[1] **deficiencies:** the absence of things needed or required
[2] **rectified:** remedied; made right
[3] **perspectives:** viewpoints; points of view
[4] **fallacies:** mistaken beliefs; logical mistakes
[5] **rhetoric:** the art of using words in writing and speaking
[6] **straw man:** a weak argument used by a speaker so that he can attack it and win an easy victory
[7] **excluded middle:** one of the laws of logic, according to which everything is either A or not-A (something or the absence of something)
[8] *non sequitur*: conclusion that doesn't follow from the premises
[9] *post hoc ergo propter hoc*: a *non sequitur* in an argument
[10] **homage:** respect; reverence
[11] **deflation:** reduction; literally, the letting out of air or gas
[12] **tenet:** belief; doctrine
[13] **chattel:** a piece of property that is not real estate

A CLOSER LOOK

1. What items on Sagan's list would you expect from a scientist? Which items on his list tell you about Sagan's personal values?

2. Which of the twelve items on the list do you feel is the most important? Why? Which is the least important? Why?

3. Which of the twelve do you feel you have already learned? Do you agree that all twelve should or could be taught in school? Explain why or why not.

● N. Scott Momaday is a modern author whose work reflects his pride in the values of his Navaho heritage. In this poem, he brings to life the joyful spirit of an individual living in harmony with the world around him.

N. Scott Momaday

THE DELIGHT SONG OF TSOAI-TALEE

I am a feather in the bright sky.
I am the blue horse that runs in the plain.
I am the fish that rolls, shining, in the water.
I am the shadow that follows a child.
I am the evening light, the lustre[1] of meadows.
I am an eagle playing with the wind.
I am a cluster of bright beads.
I am the farthest star.
I am the cold of the dawn.
I am the roaring of the rain.
I am the glitter on the crust of the snow.
I am the long track of the moon in a lake.
I am a flame of four colors.
I am a deer standing away in the dusk.
I am a field of sumac and the pomme blanche.
I am an angle of geese upon the winter sky.
I am the hunger of a young wolf.
I am the whole dream of these things.

You see, I am alive, I am alive.
I stand in good relation to the earth.
I stand in good relation to the gods.
I stand in good relation to all that is beautiful.
I stand in good relation to the daughter of Tsen-tainte.
You see, I am alive, I am alive.

[1] **lustre:** shine; inner glow

"Miss Pipkin has the rarest of qualities. She can spell."

Bob Greene

THE COUNTRY'S GOING THROUGH A ROUGH SPELL

● As a magazine columnist, Bob Greene frequently reports on the American scene and comments personally on what he has observed. In this essay, he discusses one of his pet peeves. His gripe may seem blown out of proportion at first, but follow his reasoning. Like most strong opinions, this one is part of a whole web of values.

'M IN LOVE WITH A WONDERFUL GIRL. SHE'S THIRTEEN years old, she lives in El Paso, Texas, and her name is Paige Pipkin. In an age of glamour girls and disco queens, Miss Pipkin has the rarest of qualities. She can spell.

Last week Miss Pipkin correctly spelled the word *sarcophagus* and thus won the 54th National Spelling Bee in Washington, D.C. She triumphed over a young man who misspelled the word *philippic,* and thus she finished first in the competition, which is sponsored each year by the Scripps-Howard Newspapers.

The idea of a National Spelling Bee seems somehow out of date, but I think it's great. If you deal with the written word and you receive a lot of mail, as I do, then you know that people simply can't spell anymore. It is a skill that is becoming extinct in America — people apparently feel that they don't need to know how to do it, or that it is too hard to bother with.

When I go through the mail each day, I am constantly dismayed by this trend. It is getting to the point where a letter with no misspelled words is the exception. The problem goes across the board — letters from students, letters from businessmen, letters from people in public life. Even the most prosperous executives have secretaries who can't spell. And — worst of all — I sometimes get letters from teachers, and even their letters are full of misspellings.

This may seem like a minor thing, but I don't think it is. If I know that a person can't spell, then I have trouble trusting anything else about him. If he can't even get the spelling of a word right, then why should I put any faith in his version of events, or his opinions? Obviously he is sloppy in his thinking if he can't even take the trouble to make certain of the spelling of the words he uses.

I fear I am in a minority here. I don't know if there have been any official studies done on the problem, but just from personal observation I know that, in the last decade, the ability of people to spell has diminished rapidly. And yet you hardly ever hear it discussed.

I identify with Alexander Portnoy, the fictional protagonist[1] of Philip Roth's *Portnoy's Complaint,* on this issue. In the book, Portnoy meets a beautiful, loving, affectionate woman and immediately falls for her. But he soon makes a terrible discovery about her. He finds notes she has left for the cleaning lady, and sees that each note contains five or six misspellings. It dismays him. He wants to love her, but he knows that this awful flaw rules such a thing out. He could never truly be in love with a woman who can't even spell.

Say what you will about my writing. You may think it's lousy, it may annoy you, it may even make you sick. But believe me on one thing. I am a heck of a speller. Ask any copy editor I've ever worked with. They will tell you. In the ten years I have been writing a newspaper column, I have misspelled no more than three words. And that's an outside estimate; to be truthful, I don't think I have misspelled any.

It's not such a great feat — all you have to do is look up the words you aren't sure of. Today, for example, before I turn this column in to the copy desk, I will look up *protagonist,* which was used two paragraphs above this one. It's a simple enough step, but most people aren't willing to take it. That's the worst thing about the new inability of Americans to spell. If it just had to do with misspelled words, it would be one thing. But it is symbolic of an overall lack of discipline, a readiness not to care, a willingness to be second-rate. I know it may seem like a small thing to you, but it's really not.

All the talk lately about the U.S. auto industry suffering because workmanship allegedly[2] is inferior to workmanship in Japan — that's precisely the sort of thing that starts with a nation of people who can't even spell correctly.

And it's destined to get worse. In the television age, all print skills are going to suffer, and spelling is going to be the first one to go. People are going to decide that knowing how to spell is an archaic[3] discipline,[4] and they are going to decide they can get along without it. And the worst thing is, they'll be able to. If enough people just can't spell, then businesses are going to have to employ them anyway, and try to look past this fault.

This takes us back to Paige Pipkin, the thirteen-year-old spelling champ from El Paso. For some reason, she has grown up believing that she must have enough pride in herself to be a perfect speller. It is difficult to imagine that she will ever fail in any important area of her life. You know instinctively that she is the kind of young woman who will succeed, because she cares about doing things right.

So congratulations to Miss Pipkin for winning the National Spelling Bee. If there were any justice in this world, they would have crowned her Miss America.

[1] **protagonist:** main character
[2] **allegedly:** according to reports
[3] **archaic:** ancient; old-fashioned; out-of-date
[4] **discipline:** field of study

A CLOSER LOOK

1. With what piece of "news" does Greene begin his essay? What other issues in the news does he mention? How does he connect them?

2. What personal experience does Greene bring to bear on this issue? Does this persuade you to agree with him? Why or why not?

3. Why do you think Greene feels so strongly on this issue? Do you agree with him? If so, what are your own reasons? If not, what parts of his arguments do you disagree with?

"It's our *fault*; all of us are to blame."

Andy Rooney

QUALITY

● Like Bob Greene (page 49), syndicated columnist Andy Rooney seems to be airing a personal gripe. Although he is discussing his own feelings, however, Rooney supports them with thoughtful observations on modern American life. He sounds like an ordinary "man in the street," reacting with common sense to daily life. Maybe that's why so many readers find him very convincing.

T IS SICKENING TO SEE SOMEONE MAKE A BAD product and run a good one out of business. It happens all the time, and we look around to see whose fault it is. I have a sneaking feeling we aren't looking hard enough. It's *our* fault; all of us are to blame.

If it isn't our fault — the fault of the American people — whose fault is it? Who is it that makes so many bad television shows so popular?

Why are so many good newspapers having a tough time, when the trash "newspapers" in the supermarkets are prospering? No one is forcing any of us to buy them.

Around the office I work in, they changed the paper towels several months ago. The new ones are nowhere near as good as the brand they had for years, and it takes three to do what one of the old ones would do. Somebody in the company decided it would look good if they bought cheaper paper towels. It is just incredible that smart people decide to save money in such petty ways.

I had a friend whose father owned a drugstore in a small town in

South Carolina. It was beautifully kept and well run. My friend's father was an experienced druggist who knew the whole town's medical history. During the 1950s, one of those big chain drugstores moved, in selling umbrellas, plastic beach balls, tote bags, and dirty books, and that was the end of the good, honest, little drugstore.

We are fond of repeating familiar old sayings such as, "It's quality not quantity that matters," but we don't buy as though we believe that very often. We take the jumbo size advertised at twenty percent off — no matter what the quality is. I'm glad I'm not in the business of making anything, because it must be heartbreaking for the individual making something the best way he knows how to see a competitor come in and get rich making the same thing with cheap materials and shoddy workmanship.

America's great contribution to mankind has been the invention of mass production. We showed the world how to make things quickly, inexpensively, and in such great numbers that even people who didn't have a lot of money could afford them. Automobiles were our outstanding example for a long time. We made cars that weren't Rolls-Royces, but they were good cars, and just about everyone could scrape together the money to buy one.

Somewhere, somehow, we went wrong. One by one, the good carmakers were driven out of business by another company making a cheaper one. I could have cried when Packard went out of business, but there were thirty other automobile makers that went the same way, until all that was left was General Motors, American Motors, Chrysler and Ford. And in a few years we may not have all of them.

We found a way to mass-assemble homes after World War II. We started slapping them up with cinder block and plywood, and it seemed good because a lot of people who never could afford a home before were able to buy them.

They didn't need carpenters who were master craftsmen to build those homes, and young people working on them never really got to know how to do anything but hammer a nail.

We have a lot to be proud of, but there is such a proliferation[1] of inferior products on the market now that it seems as though we have to find a way to go in another direction. The term "Made by hand" is still the classiest stamp you can put on products, and we need more of them. We need things made by people who care more about the quality of what they're making than the money they're going to get selling it.

It's our own fault, and no amount of good government, bad government, more government, or less government is going to turn us around. The only way we're going to get started in the right direction again is to stop buying junk.

---

[1] **proliferation:** increase; growing number

A CLOSER LOOK

1. What is Rooney's main gripe? What does he want us to do about it?

2. How would you describe Rooney's tone of voice? What makes this an effective writing style for this topic?

3. Make a list of the examples Rooney gives to support his opinion. What examples can you think of to add to this list? What examples can you think of to prove that "quality" is not being lost today?

● Back in the 1840s, Thoreau went to live by himself in the woods to get away from society. He kept a journal for two years and later wrote <u>Walden</u>, a book about the experience. To Thoreau, nature seemed full of lessons about how human beings should live. This poem is really a passage from his journal, printed here as verse.

Henry David Thoreau

TREES

They battle with the tempests of a century.
See what scars they bear,
What limbs they lost before we were born!

Yet they never adjourn;
They steadily vote for their principles,
And send their roots further and wider
From the *same center*.
They die at their posts,
And they leave a tough butt for the choppers
To exercise themselves about,
And a stump which serves as their monument.
They attend no caucus,[1]
They make no compromise,
They use no policy.
Their only principle is growth.

[1] **caucus:** closed meeting usually to discuss policy and choose candidates

"Here is the testament of wasters, the stain of prosperity."

Marya Mannes

WASTELAND

● Archaeologists study ancient civilizations by examining the objects they have left behind. Social critic Marya Mannes looks at modern American society with the eyes of an archaeologist, judging us by the objects with which we surround ourselves. As she pieces together a description of our culture, she asks some very tough questions.

CANS. CANS, GLINTING ON THE EDGE OF A MILLION miles of roadways, lying in scrub, grass, dirt, leaves, sand, mud, but never hidden. Cans, shining in the sun or in the beams of headlights at night. Cans washed by rain or flattened by wheels, but never dulled, never destroyed. Here is the mark of savages, the testament[1] of wasters, the stain of prosperity.

Who are these people who defile[2] the grassy borders of our roads and lanes, who pollute our ponds, who spoil the purity of our ocean beaches with the empty vessels of their thirst? Who are these people who make these vessels in millions and then say, "Drink — and discard"? What society is this that can afford to cast away a million tons of metal and to make of wild and fruitful land a garbage heap?

What manner of men and women need thirty feet of steel and two hundred horsepower to take them, singly, to their small destinations? Who demand that what they eat is wrapped so that forests are cut down to make the paper that is thrown away? Who demand that what they smoke and chew is sealed so that the sealers can be tossed in gutters and caught in twigs and grass?

"What will we leave behind us?"

What kind of men and women can afford to make the streets of their towns and cities hideous with neon at night, and their roadways hideous with signs by day, wasting beauty? What kind of people leave the carcasses of cars to rot in heaps; spill their trash into ravines and make smoking mountains of trash for the town's rats? What manner of men and women choke off the life in rivers, streams, and lakes with the waste of their produce, making poison of water?

Who is as rich as that? Slowly the wasters and despoilers[3] are impoverishing[4] our land, our nature, and our beauty, so that there will not be one beach, one hill, one lane, one meadow, one forest free from the debris of man and the stigma[5] of his improvidence.[6]

Who is so rich that he can squander[7] forever the wealth of earth and water for the trivial needs of vanity or the compulsive demands of greed? Who is so prosperous in land that he can sacrifice nature for unnatural desires? The earth we abuse and the living things we kill will, in the end, take their revenge; for in exploiting their presence we are diminishing our future.

And what will we leave behind us when we are long dead?

Temples? Amphoras?[8] Sunken treasure?

Or mountains of twisted, rusted steel, canyons of plastic containers, and a million miles of shores garlanded,[9] not with the lovely wrack[10] of the sea, but with the cans and bottles and light bulbs and boxes of a people who conserved their convenience at the expense of their heritage, and whose ephemeral[11] prosperity was built on waste.

[1] **testament:** will; tribute; statement
[2] **defile:** make impure or unclean
[3] **despoilers:** those who rob something of its value
[4] **impoverishing:** draining away the strength or richness
[5] **stigma:** stain
[6] **improvidence:** inability to see or provide for the future
[7] **squander:** waste; spend foolishly
[8] **amphoras:** ancient Greek vases
[9] **garlanded:** wreathed
[10] **wrack:** ruins
[11] **ephemeral:** short-lived

A CLOSER LOOK

1. What objects is Mannes looking at in this essay? Why are they there?

2. What would you say is Mannes' primary social criticism in this essay?

3. Does this essay examine both sides of the issue? Is it fair? What do you think was Mannes' purpose in writing it?

Martin Luther King, Jr.

A DRUM MAJOR FOR JUSTICE

● Martin Luther King, Jr., will long be remembered for his work to make America, and the world, a better place. This essay is an excerpt from Dr. King's last sermon, delivered a few days before his death in Atlanta, Georgia. His words are chilling because they seem to foretell his untimely death. But they appear here because they are also inspiring, and because they sum up the principles by which a great humanitarian lived his short but courageous life.

EVERY NOW AND THEN I GUESS WE ALL THINK realistically about that day when we will be victimized with what is life's final common denominator — that something we call death.

We all think about it, and every now and then I think about my own death and I think about my own funeral. And I don't think about it in a morbid[1] sense. And every now and then I ask myself what it is that I would want said, and I leave the word to you this morning.

If any of you are around when I have to meet my day, I don't want a long funeral.

And if you get somebody to deliver the eulogy,[2] tell him not to talk too long.

And every now and then I wonder what I want him to say.

Tell him not to mention that I have a Nobel Peace Prize — that isn't important.

Tell him not to mention that I have 300 or 400 other awards — that's not important. Tell him not to mention where I went to school.

I'd like somebody to mention that day that Martin Luther King, Jr., tried to give his life serving others.

I'd like for somebody to say that day that Martin Luther King, Jr., tried to love somebody.

I want you to say that day that I tried to be right and to walk with them. I want you to be able to say that day that I did try to feed the hungry. I want you to be able to say that day that I did try in my life to clothe the naked. I want you to say on that day that I did try in my life to visit those who were in prison. And I want you to say that I tried to love and serve humanity.

Yes, if you want to, say that I was a drum major. Say that I was a drum major for justice. Say that I was a drum major for peace. I was a drum major for righteousness.

And all of the other shallow things will not matter.

I won't have any money to leave behind. I won't have the fine and luxurious things of life to leave behind. But I just want to leave a committed life behind.

[1] **morbid:** gloomy
[2] **eulogy:** a formal statement of praise

A CLOSER LOOK

1. What does Dr. King mean when he says that death is "life's final common denominator"?

2. What does Dr. King want people to remember about him?

3. For what kinds of accomplishments would you most like to be remembered?

● We often find our own ideals embodied in other people —
not necessarily heroes, but ordinary strangers who possess a trait we
admire. In this vigorous poem, Piercy sketches the sort of person she
admires. What does this tell you about how she wants to live her
life?

Marge Piercy

TO BE OF USE

The people I love the best
jump into work head first
without dallying in the shallows
and swim with sure strokes almost out of sight.
They seem to become natives of that element,
the black sleek heads of seals
bouncing like half-submerged balls.

I love people who harness themselves, an ox to a heavy cart,
who pull like water buffalo, with massive patience,
who strain in the mud and the muck to move things forward,
who do what has to be done, again and again.

I want to be with people who submerge
in the task, who go into the fields to harvest

and work in a row and pass the bags along,
who stand in the line and haul in their places,
who are not parlor generals[1] and field deserters
but move in a common rhythm
when the food must come in or the fire be put out.

The work of the world is common as mud.
Botched, it smears the hands, crumbles to dust.
But the thing worth doing well done
has a shape that satisfies, clean and evident.
Greek amphoras[2] for wine or oil,
Hopi vases that held corn, are put in museums
but you know they were made to be used.
The pitcher cries for water to carry
and a person for work that is real.

[1] **parlor generals:** officers who fight battles from the safety of an office
[2] **amphoras:** ancient, two-handled vases or jars

"So many years!"

Robert Coles

THE OLD ONES
OF NEW MEXICO

• Most written history is about famous people and major political events. To understand what daily life was like, however, some historians have begun to record "oral history" — spoken reminiscences about the past. Social scientist Robert Coles went to New Mexico to interview people of Hispanic and Indian descent. Fascinated with what the oldest people there told him, he wrote down an oral history of a culture and lifestyle that may soon be lost forever.

HERE ARE THE WORDS OF AN ELDERLY WOMAN who has had almost no schooling. She speaks a mixture of Spanish (which I have translated) and terse[1] but forceful English. She lives in a small, isolated mountain community well to the north of Santa Fe, New Mexico, and enjoys talking with her visitor:

"Sometimes I have a moment to think. I look back and wonder where all the time has gone to. So many years! I cannot say I like to be reminded how many. My sister is three years older. She'll be eighty this May. She is glad to talk of her age. I don't like to mention mine.

"When I look at myself in the mirror a feeling of sadness comes over me. I pull at my skin and try to erase the lines, but no luck. I think back: All those years when my husband and I were young, and never worried about our health, our strength, our appearance. I don't say we always do now; but there are times when we look like ghosts of ourselves. I will see my husband noticing how weak and tired I have become, how hunched over. I pretend not to see, but once the eyes have caught something, one cannot shake the picture off. And I look at him, too. He will straighten up when he feels my glance strike him, and I quickly move away. It is too late, though. He has been told by me, without a word spoken, that he is old, and I am old, and that is our fate, to live through these last years.

"But it is not only pity we feel for ourselves. A few drops of rain and I feel grateful; the air is so fresh afterwards. I love to sit in the sun. We have the sun so often here. It is a regular visitor, a friend one can expect to see often and trust.

"I like to make tea for my husband and me. At midday we take our tea outside and sit on our bench, our backs against the wall of the house. Neither of us wants a pillow. I tell my daughters and sons that they are soft — those beach chairs here in New Mexico so far from any ocean! The bench feels strong to us, not uncomfortable. The tea warms us inside, the sun on the outside. I joke with my husband. I say we are part of the house. The adobe[2] gets baked and so do we. For the most part, though, we say nothing. It is enough to sit and be part of God's world. We hear the birds talking to each other, and are grateful they come as close to us as they do; all the more reason to keep our tongues still and hold ourselves in one place. We listen to cars going by and wonder who is rushing off. A car to us is a mystery. The young understand a car. They cannot imagine themselves not driving. They have not the interest we had in horses. Who is to compare one lifetime with another, but a horse is alive; one loves a horse and is loved by a horse. Cars come and go so fast. One year they command all eyes. The next year they are a cause for shame. The third year they must be thrown away without the slightest regret. I may exaggerate, but not much!

"The other day I thought I was going to say good-bye to this world. I was hanging up some clothes to dry. I love to do that, then stand back and watch and listen to the wind go through the socks or the pants or the dress, and see the sun warm them and make them smell fresh. I had dropped a few clothespins, and was picking them up, when suddenly I could not catch my breath, and a sharp pain seized me over my chest. I tried hard to stand up, but I couldn't. I wanted to scream but I knew there was no one nearby to hear. My husband had gone to the store. I sat down on the ground and waited. The pain was strong, and there was no one to tell about it. I felt as if someone had lassoed me and was pulling the rope tighter and tighter. Well, here you are, an old cow, being taken in by the good Lord; that is what I thought.

"I looked at myself, sitting on the ground. For a second I was my old self again — worrying about how I must have appeared there, worrying about my dress, how dirty it would get to be. This is no place for an old lady, I thought — only for one of my little grand-children, who love to play out here and build their castles of dirt, wetted down with water I give to them. Then more pain; I thought I had about a minute of life left. I said my prayers. I said good-bye to the house. I pictured my husband in my mind; fifty-seven years of marriage. Such a good man! I said to myself that I might not see him ever again. Surely God would take him into heaven, but as for me, I have no right to expect that outcome. Then I looked up to the sky and waited.

"My eye caught sight of a cloud. It was darker than the rest. It was alone. It was coming my way. The hand of God, I was sure of it! So that is how one dies. All my life, in the spare moments a person has, I wondered how I would go. Now I knew. Now I was ready. I thought I would soon be taken up to the cloud and across the sky I would go, and that would be that. But the cloud kept moving, and soon it was no longer above me, but beyond me; and I was still on my own land, so dear to me, so familiar after all these years. I can't be dead, I thought to myself. I am here and the cloud is way over there, and getting further each second. Maybe the next cloud — but by then I had decided God had other things to do. Perhaps my name had come up, but He had decided to call others before me, and get around to me later. Who can ever know His reasons? Then I spotted my neighbor walking down the road, and I said to myself that I would shout for him. I did, and he heard. But you know, by the time he came I had sprung myself free. Yes, that is right, the pain was all gone.

"He helped me up, and he was ready to go find my husband and bring him back. No, I told him, no; I was all right. I did not want to risk frightening my husband. He is excitable. He might get some kind of attack himself. I went inside and put myself down on our bed and waited. For an hour — it was that long, I am sure — my eyes stared at the ceiling, held on to it for dear life. And then he was there, my husband, calling my name and looking into my eyes with his.

"If the stars have courage, we ought to have courage."

"I'm all right," I told him. He didn't know what had happened. Our neighbor had sealed his lips, as I told him to do. But my husband knows me, so he knew I looked unusually tired; and he couldn't be easily tricked by me. The more I told him I'd just worked too hard, that is all, the more he knew I was holding something back. Finally, I pulled my ace card. I pretended to be upset by his questions and by all the attention he was giving me. I accused him: Why do you make me want to cry, why do you wish me ill, with those terrible thoughts of yours? I am not ill! If you cannot let me rest without thinking I am, then God have mercy on you for having such an imagination! God have mercy! With the second plea to our Lord, he was beaten and silent. He left me alone. I was about to beg him to come back, beg his forgiveness. But I did not want him to bear the burden of knowing; he would not rest easy by day or by night. This way he can say to himself, she has always been cranky, and she will always be cranky, so thank goodness her black moods come only now and then — a spell followed by the bright sun again.

"I will say what I think happened: I came near going, then there was a change of heart up there in heaven, so I have a few more days, or weeks, or months, or years — who knows? As for a doctor, I have never seen one, so why start now? Here we are so far away from a hospital. We have no money. We are the poor ones, the lost ones. My son tells me the Anglos look down on us — old people without education and up in the hills, trying to scrape what we can from the land, and helped only by our animals. No matter; our son is proud of us. He is proud to stay here with us. He says that if he went to the city he would beg for work and be told no, no, no. Eventually he might be permitted to sweep someone's floor. Better to hold onto one's land. Better to fight it out with the weather and the animals.

"I think of what my life has been like. It has been a simple life, a very important one, maybe an unnecessary one. I am sure there are better people, men and women all over the world, who have done more for their neighbors and yet not lived as long as I have. I feel ashamed of all the complaints I've made to myself and to my family, when the truth has been that my fate has been to live a long and healthy life, and to have a good and loyal husband, and to bring two sons and three daughters into this world.

"I think of the five children we have lost, three before they had a chance to take a breath. I wonder where in the universe they are. In the evening sometimes, when I go to close loose doors that otherwise complain loudly all night, I am likely to look at the stars and feel my long-gone infants near at hand. They are far off, I know; but in my mind they have become those stars — very small, but shining there bravely, no matter how cold it is so far up. If the stars have courage, we ought to have courage; that is what I think."

[1] **terse:** concise; polished
[2] **adobe:** a heavy clay used in making bricks

A CLOSER LOOK

1. How did this old woman react when she thought she was going to die? What seemed most important to her at that moment?

2. Look back at the woman's description of the sun, horses, clouds, and stars. How would you describe the old woman's relationship to nature?

3. In what ways do you think this woman's view of life has changed from the view she had when she was young?

● How do people describe their values? Some talk about what they don't believe in; others talk about what they do believe in. Poets often use images to describe their values. Booth contrasts two sets of images in this poem in order to define what is important in her life.

Sara Booth

ARIEL

Please don't let me get trapped
in one of those pastel worlds
where everything is white bread
iceberg lettuce
45% cotton 55% polyester
Muzak.
I want to live copper, blue-green, burgundy,
satin and sailcloth,
the sea at midnight,
the sky at noon.
Don't let me live earthbound,
with my eyes on my lawn
or in my neighbor's windows.
I want to soar
sail
splash
like a kite.
Let me frame the sky
and hang it on the wall.
Let me keep the mountains
in a box under my bed.

"He wasn't a bit ashamed of his poverty nor of his rags."

John Steinbeck

JUNIUS MALTBY

● When the values of one individual clash with the values of his or her society, which values ought to prevail? John Steinbeck asked that question in many novels and short stories. Beginning his writing career during the Depression of the 1930s, Steinbeck took society's outcasts — the down-and-outers — as his heroes. Although he portrayed them sympathetically, however, he knew that they did not always win their struggle with the rest of society.

JUNIUS MALTBY WAS A SMALL YOUNG MAN OF good and cultured family and decent education. When his father died bankrupt, Junius got himself inextricably[1] entangled in a clerkship, against which he feebly struggled for ten years.

After work Junius retired to his furnished room, patted the cushions of his morris chair[2] and spent the evening reading. Stevenson's[3] essays he thought nearly the finest things in English: he read *Travels with a Donkey* many times.

One evening soon after his thirty-fifth birthday, Junius fainted on the steps of his boarding house. When he recovered consciousness, he noticed for the first time that his breathing was difficult and unsatisfactory. He wondered how long it had been that way. The doctor whom he consulted was kind and even hopeful.

"You're by no means too far gone to get well," he said. "But you really must take those lungs out of San Francisco. If you stay here in the fog, you won't live a year. Move to a warm, dry climate."

75

The accident to his health filled Junius with pleasure, for it cut the strings he had been unable to sever for himself. He had five hundred dollars, not that he ever saved any money; he had simply forgotten to spend it.

"With that much," he said, "I'll either recover and make a clean, new start, or else I'll die and be through with the whole business."

A man in his office told him of the warm, protected valley, the Pastures of Heaven, and Junius went there immediately. The name pleased him. "It's either an omen that I'm not going to live," he thought, "or else it's a nice symbolic substitute for death." He felt that the name meant something personal to him, and he was very glad, because for ten years nothing in the world had been personal to him.

There were, in the Pastures of Heaven, several families who wanted to take boarders. Junius inspected each one, and finally went to live on the farm of the widow Quaker. She needed the money, and besides, he could sleep in a shed separated from the farmhouse. Mrs. Quaker had two small boys and kept a hired man to work the farm.

The warm climate worked tenderly with Junius' lungs. Within the year his color was good and he had gained in weight. He was quiet and happy on the farm, and what pleased him more, he had thrown out the ten years of the office and had grown superbly lazy. Junius' thin blond hair went uncombed; he wore his glasses far down on his square nose, for his eyes were getting stronger and only the habit of feeling spectacles caused him to wear them. Throughout the day he had always some small stick protruding from his mouth, a habit only the laziest and most ruminative[4] of men acquire. This convalescence took place in 1910.

In 1911, Mrs. Quaker began to worry about what the neighbors were saying. When she considered the implication of having a single man in her house, she became upset and nervous. As soon as Junius' recovery seemed sure beyond doubt, the widow confessed her trepidations.[5] He married her, immediately and gladly. Now he had a home and a golden future, for the new Mrs. Maltby owned two hundred acres of grassy hillside and five acres of orchard and vegetable bottom. Junius sent for his books, his morris chair with the adjustable back, and his good copy of Velasquez' *Cardinal*. The future was a pleasant and sunshiny afternoon to him.

76

Mrs. Maltby promptly discharged the hired man and tried to put her husband to work; but in this she encountered a resistance the more bewildering because it presented no hard front to strike at. During his convalescence, Junius had grown to love laziness. He liked the valley and the farm, but he liked them as they were: he didn't want to plant new things, nor to tear out old. When Mrs. Maltby put a hoe in his hand and set him to work in the vegetable garden, she found him, likely enough, hours later, dangling his feet in the meadow stream and reading his pocket copy of *Kidnapped*. He was sorry; he didn't know how it had happened. And that was the truth.

At first she nagged him a great deal about his laziness and sloppiness of dress, but he soon developed a faculty for never listening to her. It would be impolite, he considered, to notice her when she was not being a lady. It would be like staring at a cripple. And Mrs. Maltby, after she had battered at his resistance of fog for a time, took to sniveling and neglecting her hair.

Between 1911 and 1917, the Maltbys grew very poor. Junius simply would not take care of the farm. They even sold a few acres of pasture land to get money for food and clothing, and even then there was never enough to eat. Poverty sat cross-legged on the farm, and the Maltbys were ragged. They had never any new clothes at all, but Junius had discovered the essays of David Grayson. He wore overalls and sat under the sycamores that lined the meadow stream. Sometimes he read *Adventures in Contentment* to his wife and two sons.

Early in 1917, Mrs. Maltby found that she was going to have a baby, and late in the same year the wartime influenza epidemic struck the family with a dry viciousness. Perhaps because they were undernourished, the two boys were stricken simultaneously. For three days the house seemed filled to overflowing with flushed, feverish children whose nervous fingers strove to cling to life by the threads of their bed clothes. For three days they struggled weakly, and on the fourth, both of the boys died. Their mother didn't know it, for she was confined,[6] and the neighbors who came to help in the house hadn't the courage nor the cruelty to tell her. The black fever came upon her while she was in labor and killed her before she ever saw her child.

The neighbor women who helped at the birth told the story

throughout the valley that Junius Maltby read books by the stream while his wife and children died. But this was only partly true. On the day of their seizure, he dangled his feet in the stream because he didn't know they were ill, but thereafter he wandered vaguely from one to the other of the dying children, and talked nonsense to them. He told the eldest boy how diamonds are made. At the bedside of the other, he explained the beauty, the antiquity,[7] and the symbolism of the swastika.[8] One life went out while he read aloud the second chapter of *Treasure Island*, and he didn't even know it had happened until he finished the chapter and looked up. During those days he was bewildered. He brought out the only things he had and offered them, but they had not potency[9] with death. He knew in advance they wouldn't have, and that made it all the more terrible to him.

When the bodies were all gone, Junius went back to the stream and read a few pages of *Travels with a Donkey*. He chuckled uncertainly over the obstinacy[10] of Modestine. Who but Stevenson could have named a donkey "Modestine"?

One of the neighbor women called him in and cursed him so violently that he was embarrassed and didn't listen. She put her hands on her hips and glared at him with contempt. And then she brought his child, a son, and laid it in his arms. When she looked back at him from the gate, he was standing with the howling little brute in his arms. He couldn't see any place to put it down, so he held it for a long time.

The people of the valley told many stories about Junius. Sometimes they hated him with the loathing busy people have for lazy ones, and sometimes they envied his laziness; but often they pitied him because he blundered so. No one in the valley ever realized that he was happy.

They told how, on a doctor's advice, Junius bought a goat to milk for the baby. He didn't inquire into the sex of his purchase nor give his reason for wanting a goat. When it arrived he looked under it, and very seriously asked, "Is this a normal goat?"

"Sure," said the owner.

"But shouldn't there be a bag or something immediately behind the hind legs? — for the milk, I mean."

The people of the valley roared about that. Later, when a new and better goat was provided, Junius fiddled with it for two days and could not draw a drop of milk. He wanted to return this goat as

"He read aloud the second chapter of Treasure Island.*"*

defective until the owner showed him how to milk it. Some people claimed that he held the baby under the goat and let it suck its own milk, but this was untrue. The people of the valley declared they didn't know how he ever reared the child.

One day Junius went into Monterey and hired an old German to help him on the farm. He gave his new servant five dollars on account, and never paid him again. Within two weeks the hired man was so entangled in laziness that he did no more work than his employer. The two of them sat around the place together discussing things which interested and puzzled them — how color comes to flowers — whether there is a symbology[11] in nature — where Atlantis lay — how the Incas interred[12] their dead.

In the spring they planted potatoes, always too late, and without a covering of ashes to keep the bugs out. They sowed beans and corn and peas, watched them for a time, and then forgot them. The weeds covered everything from sight. It was no unusual thing to see Junius burrow into a perfect thicket of mallow weeds and emerge carrying a pale cucumber. He had stopped wearing shoes because he liked the feeling of the warm earth on his feet, and because he had no shoes.

In the afternoon Junius talked to Jakob Stutz a great deal. "You know," he said, "when the children died, I thought I had reached a peculiar high peak of horror. Then, almost while I thought it, the horror turned to sorrow and the sorrow dwindled to sadness. I didn't know my wife nor the children very well, I guess. Perhaps they were too near to me. It's a strange thing, this *knowing*. It is nothing but an awareness of details. There are long visioned minds and short visioned. I've never been able to see things that are close to me. For instance, I am much more aware of the Parthenon[13] than of my own house over there." Suddenly Junius' face seemed to quiver with feeling, and his eyes brightened with enthusiasm. "Jakob," he said, "have you ever seen a picture of the frieze[14] of the Parthenon?"

"Yes, and it is good, too," said Jakob.

Junius laid a hand on his hired man's knee. "Those horses," he said. "Those lovely horses — bound for a celestial[15] pasture. Those eager and yet dignified young men setting out for an incredible fiesta that's being celebrated just around the cornice.[16] I wonder how a man can know what a horse feels like when it is very happy; and that sculptor must have known or he couldn't have carved them so."

That was the way it went. Junius could not stay on a subject. Often the men went hungry because they failed to find a hen's nest in the grass when it came suppertime.

The son of Junius was named Robert Louis. Junius called him that when he thought of it, but Jakob Stutz rebelled at what he considered a kind of literary preciousness. "Boys must be named like dogs," he maintained. "One sound is sufficient for the name. Even Robert is too long. He should be called 'Bob.' " Jakob nearly got his way.

"I'll compromise with you," said Junius. "We'll call him Robbie. Robbie is really shorter than Robert, don't you think?"

He often gave way before Jakob, for Jakob continually struggled a little against the webs that were being spun about him. Now and then, with a kind of virtuous fury, he cleaned the house.

Robbie grew up gravely. He followed the men about, listening to their discussions. Junius never treated him like a little boy, because he didn't know how little boys should be treated. If Robbie made an observation the two men listened courteously and included the remark in their conversation, or even used it as the germ of an investigation. They tracked down many things in the course of an afternoon. Every day there were several raids on Junius' encyclopedia.

A huge sycamore put out a horizontal limb over the meadow stream, and on it the three sat, the men hanging their feet into the water and moving pebbles with their toes while Robbie tried extravagantly to imitate them. Reaching the water was one of his criteria of manhood. Jakob had by this time given up shoes; Robbie had never worn any in his life.

The discussions were erudite.[17] Robbie couldn't use childish talk, for he had never heard any. They didn't make conversation; rather they let a seedling of thought sprout by itself, and then watched with wonder while it sent out branching limbs. They were surprised at the strange fruit their conversation bore, for they didn't direct their thinking, not trellis nor trim it the way so many people do.

There on the limb the three sat. Their clothes were rags and their hair was only hacked off to keep it out of their eyes. The men wore long, untrimmed beards. They watched the water-skaters on the surface of the pool below them, a pool which had been deepened by idling toes. The giant tree above them whisked softly in the wind, and occasionally dropped a leaf like a brown handkerchief. Robbie was five years old.

"I think sycamore trees are good," he observed when a leaf fell in his lap. Jakob picked up the leaf and stripped the parchment from its ribs.

"Yes," he agreed, "they grow by water. Good things love water. Bad things always been dry."

"Sycamores are big and good," said Junius. "It seems to me that good things are always destroyed by evil little things. Rarely is a big thing poisonous or treacherous. For this reason, in human thinking, bigness is an attribute of good and littleness of evil. Do you see that, Robbie?"

"Yes," said Robbie. "I see that. Like elephants."

"Elephants are often evil, but when we think of them, they seem gentle and good."

"But water," Jakob broke in. "Do you see about water, too?"

"No, not about water."

"But I see," said Junius. "You mean that water is the seed of life. Of the three elements water is the sperm, earth the womb, and

"I don't want to go at all."

sunshine the mold of growth." Thus they taught him nonsense.

The people of the Pastures of Heaven recoiled from Junius Maltby after the death of his wife and his two boys. Stories of his callousness[18] during the epidemic grew to such proportions that eventually they fell down of their own weight and were nearly forgotten. But although his neighbors forgot that Junius had read while his children died, they could not forget the problem he was becoming. Here in the fertile valley he lived in fearful poverty. While other families built small fortunes, bought Fords and radios, put in electricity and went twice a week to the moving pictures in Monterey or Salinas, Junius degenerated and became a ragged savage. The men of the valley resented his good bottom land, all overgrown with weeds, his untrimmed fruit trees and his fallen fences. The women thought with loathing of his unclean house with its littered dooryard and dirty windows. Both men and women hated his idleness and his complete lack of pride. For a while they went to visit him, hoping by their neat examples to drag him from his slothfulness.[19] But he received them naturally and with the friendliness of equality. He wasn't a bit ashamed of his poverty nor of his rags. Gradually his neighbors came to think of Junius as an outcast. No one drove up the private road to his house any more. They outlawed him from decent society and resolved never to receive him should he visit them.

Junius knew nothing about the dislike of his neighbors. He was still gloriously happy. His life was as unreal, as romantic, and as unimportant as his thinking. He was content to sit in the sun and to dangle his feet in the stream. If he had no good clothes, at least he had no place to go which required good clothes.

Although the people almost hated Junius, they had only pity for the little boy Robbie. The women told one another how horrible it was to let the child grow up in such squalor.[20] But, because they were mostly good people, they felt a strong reluctance for interfering with Junius' affairs.

"Wait until he's school age," Mrs. Banks said to a group of ladies in her own parlor. "We couldn't do anything now if we wanted to. He belongs to that father of his. But just as soon as the child is six, the country'll have something to say, let me tell you."

Mrs. Allen nodded and closed her eyes earnestly. "We keep forgetting that he's Mamie Quaker's child as much as Maltby's. I think we should have stepped in long ago. But when he goes to school we'll give the poor little fellow a few things he never had."

"The least we can do is to see that he has enough clothes to cover him," another of the women agreed.

It seemed that the valley lay crouched in waiting for the time when Robbie should go to school. When, at term opening, after his sixth birthday, he did not appear, John Whiteside, the clerk of the school board, wrote a letter to Junius Maltby.

"I hadn't thought of it," Junius said when he read it. "I guess you'll have to go to school."

"I don't want to go," said Robbie.

"I know. I don't much want you to go, either. But we have laws. The law has a self-protective appendage called penalty. We have to balance the pleasure of breaking the law against the punishment. The Carthaginians[21] punished even misfortune. If a general lost a battle through bad luck, he was executed. At present we punish people for accidents of birth and circumstance in much the same manner."

In the ensuing discussion they forgot all about the letter. John Whiteside wrote a very curt note.

"Well, Robbie, I guess you'll have to go," said Junius, when he received it. "Of course they'll teach many useful things."

"Why don't you teach me?" Robbie pleaded

"Oh, I can't. You see I've forgotten the things they teach."

"I don't want to go at all. I don't want to learn things."

"I know you don't, but I can't see any other way out."

And so one morning Robbie trudged to school. He was clad in an ancient pair of overalls, out at the knees and seat, a blue shirt from which the collar was gone, and nothing else. His long hair hung over his gray eyes like the forelock of a range pony.

The children made a circle around him in the school yard and stared at him in silence. They had all heard of the poverty of the Maltbys and of Junius' laziness. The boys looked forward to this moment when they could torture Robbie. Here was the time come; he stood in their circle, and they only stared at him. No one said, "Where'd you get them clothes," or, "Look at his hair," the way they had intended to. The children were puzzled by their failure to torment Robbie.

As for Robbie, he regarded the circle with serious eyes. He was not in the least frightened. "Don't you play games?" he asked. "My father said you'd play games."

And then the circle broke up with howls. "He doesn't know any games." — "Let's teach him pewee." "Listen! Listen! Prisoner's base first." — "He doesn't know any games."

And, although they didn't know why, they thought it rather a fine thing not to know games. Robbie's thin face was studious. "We'll try pewee first," he decided. He was clumsy at the new games, but his teachers did not hoot at him. Instead they quarreled for the privilege of showing him how to hold the pewee stick. There are several schools of technique in pewee. Robbie stood aside listening for a while, and at last chose his own instructor.

Robbie's effect on the school was immediate. The older boys let him entirely alone, but the younger ones imitated him in everything, even tearing holes in the knees of their overalls. When they sat in the sun with their backs to the school wall, eating their lunches, Robbie told them about his father and about the sycamore tree. They listened intently and wished their fathers were lazy and gentle, too.

Sometimes a few of the boys, disobeying the orders of their parents, sneaked up to the Maltby place on a Saturday. Junius gravitated naturally to the sycamore limb, and, while they sat on both sides of him, he read *Treasure Island* to them, or described the

Gallic wars or the battle of Trafalgar. In no time at all, Robbie, with the backing of his father, became the king of the school yard. This is demonstrated by the facts that he had no chum, that they gave him no nickname, and that he arbitrated all the disputes. So exalted was his station that no one even tried to fight with him.

Only gradually did Robbie come to realize that he was the leader of the younger boys of the school. Something self-possessed and mature about him made his companions turn to him for leadership. It wasn't long before his was the voice which decided the game to be played. In baseball he was the umpire for the reason that no other boy could make a ruling without causing a riot. And while he played the games badly himself, questions of rules and ethics were invariably referred to him.

After a lengthy discussion with Junius and Jakob, Robbie invented two vastly popular games, one called Slinkey Coyote, a local version of Hare and Hounds, and the other named Broken Leg, a kind of glorified tag. For these two games he made rules as he needed them.

Miss Morgan's interest was aroused by the little boy, for he was as much a surprise in the schoolroom as he was in the yard. He could read perfectly and used a man's vocabulary, but he could not write. He was familiar with numbers, no matter how large, yet he refused to learn even the simplest arithmetic. Robbie learned to write with the greatest of difficulty. His hand wavered crazy letters on his school pad. At length Miss Morgan tried to help him.

"Take one thing and do it over and over until you get it perfectly," she suggested. "Be very careful with each letter."

Robbie searched his memory for something he liked. At length he wrote, "There is nothing so monsterous but we can belief it of ourselfs." He loved that monsterous. It gave timbre[22] and profundity to the thing. If there were words, which through their very sound-power could drag unwilling genii from the earth, "monsterous" was surely one of them. Over and over he wrote the sentence, putting the greatest of care and drawing on his "monsterous." At the end of an hour, Miss Morgan came to see how he was getting on.

"Why, Robert, where in the world did you hear that?"

"It's from Stevenson, ma'am. My father knows it by heart almost."

Of course Miss Morgan had heard all the bad stories of Junius, and in spite of them had approved of him. But now she began to have a strong desire to meet him. . . .

Hallowe'en went past, and Thanksgiving. In that time Robbie's effect on the boys was indicated by a growth in their vocabularies, and by a positive hatred for shoes or of any kind of good clothing for that matter. Although he didn't realize it, Robbie had set a style, not new, perhaps, but more rigid than it had been. It was unmanly to wear good clothes, and even more than that, it was considered an insult to Robbie.

One Friday afternoon Robbie wrote fourteen notes and secretly passed them to fourteen boys in the school yard. The notes were all the same. They said: "A lot of Indians are going to burn the Pres. of the U.S. to the stake at my house tomorrow at ten o'clock. Sneak out and bark like a fox down by our lower field. I will come and lead you to rescue of this poor soul."

For several months Miss Morgan had intended to call upon Junius Maltby. The stories told of him, and her contact with his son, had raised her interest to a high point. Every now and then, in the schoolroom, one of the boys imparted a piece of astounding information. For example, one child who was really famous for his stupidity, told her that Hengest and Horsa invaded Britain. When pressed he admitted that the information came from Junius Maltby, and that in some way it was a kind of a secret. The old story of the goat amused the teacher so much that she wrote it for a magazine, but no magazine bought it. Over and over she had set a date to walk out to the Maltby farm.

She awakened on a December Saturday morning and found frost in the air and a brilliant sun shining. After breakfast she put on her corduroy skirt and her hiking boots, and left the house. In the yard she tried to persuade the ranch dogs to accompany her, but they only flopped their tails and went back to sleep in the sun.

The Maltby place lay about two miles away in the little canyon called Gato Amarillo. A stream ran beside the road, and sword ferns grew rankly[23] under the alders. It was almost cold in the canyon, for the sun had not yet climbed over the mountain. Once during her walk Miss Morgan thought she heard footsteps and voices ahead of her, but when she hurried around the bend, no one was in sight. However, the brush beside the road crackled mysteriously.

Although she had never been there before, Miss Morgan knew the Maltby land when she came to it. Fences reclined tiredly on the ground under an overload of bramble. The fruit trees stretched bare

"You're dreaming. Such things just can't happen."

branches clear of a forest of weeds. Wild blackberry vines clambered up the apple trees; squirrels and rabbits bolted from under her feet, and soft-voiced doves flew away with whistling wings. In a tall wild pear tree a congress of bluejays squawked a cacophonous[24] argument. Then, beside an elm tree which wore a shaggy coat of frost-bitten morning glory, Miss Morgan saw the mossy, curled shingles of the Maltby roof. The place, in its quietness, might have been deserted for a hundred years. "How rundown and slovenly,"[25] she thought. "How utterly lovely and slipshod!" She let herself into the yard through a wicket gate which hung to its post by one iron band. The farm buildings were gray with weathering, and, up the sides of the walls, outlawed climbers[26] pushed their fingers. Miss Morgan turned the corner of the house and stopped in her tracks; her mouth fell open and a chill shriveled on her spine. In the center of the yard a stout post was set up, and to it an old and ragged man was bound with many lengths of rope. Another man, younger and smaller, but even more ragged, piled brush about the feet of the captive. Miss Morgan shivered and backed around the house corner again. "Such things don't happen," she insisted. "You're dreaming. Such things just can't happen." And then she heard the most amiable of conversations going on between the two men.

"It's nearly ten," said the torturer.

The captive replied, "Yes, and you be careful how you put fire to that brush. You be sure to see them coming before you light it."

Miss Morgan nearly screamed with relief. She walked a little unsteadily toward the stake. The free man turned and saw her. For a second he seemed surprised, but immediately recovering, he bowed. Coming from a man with torn overalls and a matted beard, the bow was ridiculous and charming.

"I'm the teacher," Miss Morgan explained breathlessly. "I was just out for a walk, and I saw this house. For a moment I thought this auto-da-fe[27] was serious."

Junius smiled. "But it *is* serious. It's more serious than you think. For a moment I thought you were the rescue. The relief is due at ten o'clock, you know."

A savage barking of foxes broke out below the house among the willows. "That will be the relief," Junius continued. "Pardon me, Miss Morgan, isn't it? I am Junius Maltby and this gentleman on ordinary days is Jakob Stutz. Today, though, he is the President of the United States being burned by Indians. For a time we thought he'd be Guenevere, but even without the full figure, he makes a better President than a Guenevere, don't you think? Besides he refused to wear a skirt."

"What foolishness," said the President complacently.[28]

Miss Morgan laughed. "May I watch the rescue, Mr. Maltby?"

"I'm not Mr. Maltby, I'm three hundred Indians."

The barking of foxes broke out again. "Over by the steps," said the three hundred Indians. He gazed toward the stream. A willow branch was shaking wildly. Junius scratched a match on his trousers and set fire to the brush at the foot of the stake. As the flame leaped up, the willow trees seemed to burst into pieces and each piece became a shrieking boy. The mass charged forward, armed as haphazardly and as terribly as the French people were when they stormed the Bastille.[29] Even as the fire licked toward the President, it was kicked violently aside. The rescuers unwound the ropes with fervent hands, and Jakob Stutz stood free and happy. Nor was the following ceremony less impressive than the rescue. As the boys stood at salute, the President marched down the line and to each overall bib pinned a leaden slug on which the word hero was deeply scratched. The game was over.

"Next Saturday we hang the guilty villains who have attempted this dastardly[30] plot," Robbie announced.

"Why not now? Let's hang 'em now!" the troop screamed.

"No, my men. There are lots of things to do. We have to make a gallows." He turned to his father. "I guess we'll have to hang both of you," he said. For a moment he looked covetously at Miss Morgan, and then reluctantly gave her up.

That afternoon was one of the most pleasant Miss Morgan had ever spent. Although she was given a seat of honor on the sycamore limb, the boys had ceased to regard her as the teacher.

"It's nicer if you take off your shoes," Robbie invited her, and it was nicer, she found, when her boots were off and her feet dangled in the water.

That afternoon Junius talked of cannibal societies among the Aleutian Indians. He told how the mercenaries turned against Carthage. He described the Lacedaemonians combing their hair before they died at Thermopylae. He explained the origin of macaroni, and told of the discovery of copper as though he had been there. Finally, the boys started for home. Miss Morgan allowed them to distance her, for she wanted to think quietly about the strange gentleman.

The day when the school board visited was looked forward to with terror by both the teacher and her pupils. It was a day of tense ceremony. Lessons were recited nervously and the misspelling of a word seemed a capital crime. There was no day on which the children made more blunders, nor on which the teacher's nerves were thinner worn.

The school board of the Pastures of Heaven visited on the afternoon of December 15. Immediately after lunch they filed in, looking somber and funereal and a little ashamed. First came John Whiteside, the clerk, old and white-haired, with an easy attitude toward education which was sometimes criticized in the valley. Pat Humbert came after him. Pat was elected because he wanted to be. He was a lonely man who had no initiative in meeting people, and who took every possible means to be thrown into their contact. His clothes were as uncompromising, as unhappy as the bronze suit on the seated statue of Lincoln in Washington. T. B. Allen followed, dumpily rolling up the aisle. Since he was the only merchant in the valley, his seat on the board belonged to him by right. Behind him strode Raymond Banks, big and jolly and very red of hands and face. Last in the line was Bert Munroe, the newly elected member. Since it was his first visit to the school, Bert seemed a little sheepish as he followed the other members to their seats at the front of the room.

When the board was seated magisterially,[31] their wives came in and found seats at the back of the room, behind the children. The pupils squirmed uneasily. They felt that they were surrounded, that escape, should they need to escape, was cut off. When they twisted in their seats, they saw that the women were smiling benevolently on them. They caught sight of a large paper bundle which Mrs. Munroe held on her lap.

School opened. Miss Morgan, with a strained smile on her face, welcomed the school board. "We will do nothing out of the ordinary, gentlemen," she said. "I think it will be more interesting to you in your official capacities to see the school as it operates every day." Very little later, she wished she hadn't said that. Never within her recollection had she seen such stupid children. Those who did manage to force words past their frozen palates made the most hideous mistakes. Their spelling was abominable. Their reading sounded like the gibbering of the insane. The board tried to be dignified, but they could not help smiling a little from embarrassment for the children. A light perspiration formed on Miss Morgan's forehead. She had visions of being dismissed from her position by an outraged board. The wives in the rear smiled on, nervously, and time dripped by. When the arithmetic had been muddled and travestied,[32] John Whiteside arose from his chair.

"Thank you, Miss Morgan," he said. "If you'll allow it, I'll just say a few words to the children, and then you can dismiss them. They ought to have some payment for having us here."

The teacher sighed with relief. "Then you do understand they weren't doing as well as usual? I'm glad you know that."

John Whiteside smiled. He had seen so many nervous young teachers on school board days. "If I thought they were doing their best, I'd close the school," he said. Then he spoke to the children for five minutes — told them they should study hard and love their teacher. It was the short and painless little speech he had used for years. The older pupils had heard it often. When it was done, he asked the teacher to dismiss the school. The pupils filed quietly out, but once in the air, their relief was too much for them. With howls and shrieks they did their best to kill each other by disembowelment

90

and decapitation.

John Whiteside shook hands with Miss Morgan. "We've never had a teacher who kept better order," he said kindly. "I think if you knew how much the children like you, you'd be embarrassed."

"But they're good children," she insisted loyally. "They're awfully good children."

"Of course," John Whiteside agreed. "By the way, how is the little Maltby boy getting along?"

"Why, he's a bright youngster, a curious child. I think he has almost a brilliant mind."

"We've been talking about him in board meeting, Miss Morgan. You know, of course, that his home life isn't all that it ought to be. I noticed him this afternoon especially. The poor child's hardly clothed."

"Well, it's a strange home." Miss Morgan felt that she had to defend Junius. "It's not the usual kind of home, but it isn't bad."

"Don't mistake me, Miss Morgan. We aren't going to interfere. We just thought we ought to give him a few things. His father's very poor, you know."

"I know," she said gently.

"Mrs. Munroe bought him a few clothes. If you'll call him in, we'll give them to him."

"Oh. No, I wouldn't — " she began.

"Why not? We only have a few little shirts and a pair of overalls and some shoes."

"But Mr. Whiteside, it might embarrass him. He's quite a proud little chap."

"Embarrass him to have decent clothes? Nonsense! I should think it would embarrass him more not to have them. But aside from that, it's too cold for him to go barefoot at this time of year. There's been frost on the ground every morning for a week."

"I wish you wouldn't," she said helplessly. "I really wish you wouldn't do it."

"Miss Morgan, don't you think you're making too much of this? Mrs. Munroe has been kind enough to buy the things for him. Please call him in so she can give them to him."

A moment later Robbie stood before them. His unkempt hair fell over his face, and his eye still glittered with the fierceness of the play in the yard. The group gathered at the front of the room regarded him kindly, trying not to look too pointedly at his ragged

"I think he has almost a brilliant mind."

clothes. Robbie gazed uneasily about.

"Mrs. Munroe has something to give you, Robert," Miss Morgan said.

Then Mrs. Munroe came forward and put the bundle in his arms. "What a nice little boy!"

Robbie placed the package carefully on the floor and put his hands behind him.

"Open it, Robert," T. B. Allen said sternly. "Where are your manners?"

Robbie gazed resentfully at him. "Yes, sir," he said, and untied the string. The shirts and the new overalls lay open before him, and he stared at them uncomprehendingly. Suddenly he seemed to realize what they were. His face flushed warmly. For a moment he looked about nervously like a trapped animal, and then he bolted through the door, leaving the little heap of clothing behind him. The school board heard two steps on the porch, and Robbie was gone.

Mrs. Munroe turned helplessly to the teacher. "What's wrong with him, anyway?"

"I think he was embarrassed," said Miss Morgan.

"But why should he be? We were nice to him."

The teacher tried to explain, and became a little angry with them in trying. "I think, you see — why I don't think he ever knew he was poor until a moment ago."

"It was my mistake," John Whiteside apologized. "I'm sorry, Miss Morgan."

"What can we do about him?" Bert Munroe asked.

"I don't know. I really don't know."

Mrs. Munroe turned to her husband. "Bert, I think if you went out and had a talk with Mr. Maltby it might help. I don't mean you to be anything but kind. Just tell him little boys shouldn't walk around in bare feet in the frost. Maybe just a word like that'll help. Mr. Maltby could tell little Robert he must take the clothes. What do you think, Mr. Whiteside?"

"I don't like it. You'll have to vote to overrule my objection. I've done enough harm."

"I think his health is more important than his feelings," Mrs. Munroe insisted.

School closed for Christmas week on the twentieth of December. Miss Morgan planned to spend her vacation in Los Angeles. While she waited at the crossroads for a bus to Salinas, she saw a man and a little boy walking down the Pastures of Heaven road toward her. They were dressed in cheap new clothes, and both of them walked as though their feet were sore. As they neared her, Miss Morgan looked closely at the little boy, and saw that it was Robbie. His face was sullen and unhappy.

"Why, Robert," she cried. "What's the matter? Where are you going?"

The man spoke. "We're going to San Francisco, Miss Morgan."

She looked up quickly. It was Junius shorn of his beard. She hadn't realized that he was so old. Even his eyes, which had been young, looked old. But of course he was pale because the beard had protected his skin from sunburn. On his face there was a look of deep puzzlement.

"Are you going up for the Holidays?" Miss Morgan asked. "I love the stores in the city around Christmas. I could look in them for days."

"No," Junius replied slowly. "I guess we're going to be up there for good. I am an accountant, Miss Morgan. At least I was an

93

"I'm going to try to get a job."

accountant twenty years ago. I'm going to try to get a job." There was pain in his voice.

"But why do you do that?" she demanded.

"You see," he explained simply, "I didn't know I was doing an injury to the boy, here. I hadn't thought about it. I suppose I should have thought about it. You can see that he shouldn't be brought up in poverty. You can see that, can't you? I didn't know what people were saying about us."

"Why don't you stay on the ranch? It's a good ranch, isn't it?"

"But I couldn't make a living on it, Miss Morgan. I don't know anything about farming. Jakob is going to try to run the ranch, but you know, Jakob is very lazy. Later, when I can, I'll sell the ranch so Robbie can have a few things he never had."

Miss Morgan was angry, but at the same time she felt she was going to cry. "You don't believe everything silly people tell you, do you?"

The bus came into sight on the highway and bore down on them. Junius pointed to Robbie. "He didn't want to come. He ran away into the hills. Jakob and I caught him last night. He's lived like a little animal too long, you see. Besides, Miss Morgan, he doesn't know how nice it will be in San Francisco."

The bus squealed to a stop. Junius and Robbie climbed into the back seat. Miss Morgan was about to get in beside them. Suddenly she turned and took her seat beside the driver. "Of course," she said to herself. "Of course, they want to be alone."

---

[1] **inextricably:** done in a way that it's impossible to free oneself
[2] **morris chair:** an easy chair with an adjustable back and removable cushions
[3] **Stevenson, Robert Louis** (1850-1894): author of *Treasure Island*
[4] **ruminative:** reflective; thoughtful
[5] **trepidations:** fears
[6] **confined:** undergoing childbirth
[7] **antiquity:** age
[8] **swastika:** an ancient symbol; Steinbeck wrote his story before the swastika became the symbol of Nazi Germany
[9] **potency:** strength
[10] **obstinacy:** stubbornness
[11] **symbology:** symbolism
[12] **interred:** buried
[13] **Parthenon:** Greek temple in Athens
[14] **frieze:** sculpture on a building
[15] **celestial:** heavenly
[16] **cornice:** the molding that crowns a building

[17] **erudite:** wise; educated; learned
[18] **callousness:** lack of feeling
[19] **slothfulness:** laziness
[20] **squalor:** dirt; filth
[21] **Carthaginians:** people of ancient Carthage in North Africa
[22] **timbre:** tone; resonance
[23] **rankly:** luxuriently; excessively; in overabundance
[24] **cacophonous:** harsh-sounding
[25] **slovenly:** messy; not neat or clean
[26] **climbers:** vines
[27] **auto-da-fe:** the burning of a heretic (a person who disagrees with accepted beliefs)
[28] **complacently:** calmly; with self-satisfaction
[29] **Bastille:** the French stormed this prison at the start of the French Revolution
[30] **dastardly:** cowardly
[31] **magisterially:** in a dignified and formal way
[32] **travestied:** imitated in an absurd or funny way

A CLOSER LOOK

1. What caused Junius Maltby's first great change in life? What caused his second great change?

2. Describe Miss Morgan's personality. Why is she an important character in this story?

3. Would you say Junius Maltby was a good father or a bad one? Use examples from the story to explain your answer.

● Whitman's unrhymed, sprawling verse marked him as a rebel among nineteenth-century poets. In his ideas, too, he rebelled against the formal, stuffy customs of his times. In this short poem, he compares his own feelings about the stars to the formal, scientific interpretation of an astronomer.

Walt Whitman

WHEN I HEARD THE LEARN'D ASTRONOMER

When I heard the learn'd astronomer,
When the proofs, the figures, were ranged in columns before me,
When I was shown the charts and diagrams, to add, divide,
    and measure them,
When I sitting heard the astronomer where he lectured with
    much applause in the lecture-room,
How soon unaccountable I became tired and sick,
Till rising and gliding out I wander'd off by myself,
In the mystical moist night-air, and from time to time,
Look'd up in perfect silence at the stars.

"I heard a feeble wail, which seemed to come out of the earth."

Herman Melville

WHAT REDBURN SAW

● As a penniless young man, Melville traveled around the globe, working as a common sailor. After he returned home, he wrote about his adventures in dashing seafaring novels, the greatest of which was Moby Dick. To Melville's nineteenth-century readers, many of the lands he had visited seemed primitive and exotic. But Melville was not just a travel writer — he was a student of human nature. Sometimes he found strange and savage behavior even in a "civilized" country, as you'll see for yourself in this chapter from the novel Redburn.

I N GOING TO OUR BOARDING-HOUSE, I GENERALLY passed through a narrow street called "Launcelott's-Hey," which was lined with dingy, prison-like cotton warehouses. In this street, or rather alley, you seldom see anyone but a truckman or some solitary old warehouse-keeper, haunting his smoky den like a ghost.

Once, passing through this place, I heard a feeble wail, which seemed to come out of the earth. It was but a strip of crooked sidewalk where I stood. The dingy wall was on every side, converting the mid-day into twilight. Not a soul was in sight. I started, and could almost have run, when I heard that dismal sound. It seemed the low, hopeless, endless wail of someone forever lost. At last I advanced to an opening which communicated downward with deep tiers of cellars beneath a crumbling old warehouse. There, some fifteen feet below the walk, crouching in nameless squalor,[1] with her head bowed over, was the figure of what had been a woman. Her blue arms folded to her livid[2] bosom two shrunken things like children, that leaned toward her, one on each side. At first, I knew not whether they were alive or dead. They made no sign; they did not move or stir; but from the vault came that soul-sickening wail.

I made a noise with my foot, which, in the silence, echoed far and near, but there was no response. Louder still; when one of the children lifted its head and cast upward a faint glance, then closed its eyes and lay motionless. The woman also now gazed up, and perceived me; but let fall her eye again. They were dumb and next to dead with want. How they had crawled into that den, I could not tell; but there they had crawled to die. At that moment I never thought of relieving them; for death was so stamped in their glazed and unimploring[3] eyes, that I almost regarded them as already no more. I stood looking down on them, while my whole soul swelled within me; and I asked myself, what right had anybody in the wide world to smile and be glad, when sights like this were to be seen. It was enough to turn the heart to gall.[4] For who were these ghosts that I saw? Were they not human beings? A woman and two girls? With eyes, and lips, and ears like any queen? With hearts which, though they did not bound with blood, yet beat with a dull, dead ache that was their life?

At last, I walked on toward an open lot in the alley. I hoped to meet there some ragged old women, whom I had daily noticed groping amid foul rubbish for little particles of dirty cotton, which they washed out and sold for a trifle.

I found them. Accosting one, I asked if she knew of the persons I had just left. She replied that she did not; nor did she want to. I then asked another, a miserable, toothless old woman, with a tattered strip of coarse baling stuff round her body. Looking at me for an instant, she resumed her raking in the rubbish. She said that she knew whom it was that I spoke of, but that she had no time to attend to beggars and their brats. Accosting still another, who seemed to know my errand, I asked if there was no place to which the woman could be taken. "Yes," she replied, "to the churchyard." I said she was alive, and not dead.

"Then she'll never die," was the rejoinder. "She's been down there these three days, with nothing to eat; — that I know myself."

"She deserves it," said an old hag, who was just placing on her crooked shoulders her bag of pickings, and who was turning to totter off, "that Betsy Jennings deserves it — was she ever married? Tell me that."

Leaving Launcelott's-Hey, I turned into a more frequented street, and soon meeting a policeman, told him of the condition of the woman and the girls.

"It's none of my business, Jack," said he. "I don't belong to that street."

"Who does, then?"

"I don't know. But what business is it of yours? Are you not a Yankee?"

"Yes," said I, "but come, I will help you remove that woman, if you say so."

"There, now, Jack, go on board your ship and stick to it; and leave these matters to the town."

I accosted two more policemen, but with no better success. They would not even go with me to the place. The truth was it was out of the way, in a silent, secluded spot. The misery of the three outcasts, hiding away in the ground, did not obtrude[5] upon anyone.

Returning to them, I again stamped to attract their attention; but this time, none of the three looked up, or even stirred. While I yet stood undecided, a voice called to me from a high, iron-shuttered window in a loft over the way and asked what I was about. I beckoned to the man, a sort of porter, to come down, which he did; when I pointed down into the vault.

"Well," said he, "what of it?"

"Can't we get them out?" said I. "Haven't you some place in your warehouse where you can put them? Have you nothing for them to eat?"

"You're crazy, boy," said he; "do you suppose that Parkins and Wood want their warehouse turned into a hospital?"

I then went to my boarding-house, and told Handsome Mary what I had seen. I asked her if she could not do something to get the woman and girls removed; or if she could not do that, let me have some food for them. But though a kind person in the main, Mary replied that she gave away enough to beggars in her own street (which was true enough) without looking after the whole neighborhood.

Going into the kitchen, I accosted the cook, a little shriveled-up old Welshwoman with a saucy tongue, and begged her to give me some cold victuals,[6] if she had nothing better, to take to the vault. But she broke out in a storm of swearing at the miserable occupants of the vault, and refused. I then stepped into the room where our dinner was being spread; and waiting till the girl had gone out, I

"Can't we get them out?"

snatched some bread and cheese from a stand. Thrusting it into the bosom of my frock, I left the house. Hurrying to the lane, I dropped the food down into the vault. One of the girls caught at it convulsively,[7] but fell back, apparently fainting. The sister pushed the other's arm aside and took the bread in her hand, but with a weak, uncertain grasp like an infant's. She placed it to her mouth, but let it fall again, murmuring faintly something like "water." The woman did not stir; her head was bowed over, just as I had first seen her.

Seeing how it was, I ran down toward the docks to a mean little sailor tavern, and begged for a pitcher; but the cross old man who kept it refused, unless I would pay for it. But I had no money. My boarding-house was some way off, and it would be lost time to run back to the ship, so, under the impulse of the moment, I hurried to a hydrant. Taking off a new hat, which had been loaned me that day, I filled it with water.

With this, I returned to Launcelott's-Hey. With considerable difficulty, like getting down into a well, I descended with it into the vault, where there was hardly space enough left to let me stand. The two girls drank out of the hat together, looking up at me with an unalterable, idiotic expression that almost made me faint. The

102

woman spoke not a word, and did not stir. While the girls were breaking and eating the bread, I tried to lift the woman's head; but, feeble as she was, she seemed bent upon holding it down. Observing her arms still clasped upon her bosom, and that something seemed hidden under the rags there, a thought crossed my mind. When I forcibly withdrew her hands for a moment, I caught a glimpse of a meager little babe, the lower part of its body thrust into an old bonnet. Its face was dazzlingly white, even in its squalor; but the closed eyes looked like balls of indigo.[8] It must have been dead some hours.

Since the woman refused to speak, eat, or drink, I asked one of the girls who they were, and where they lived; but she only stared vacantly, muttering something that could not be understood.

The air of the place was now getting too much for me; but I stood deliberating a moment, whether it was possible for me to drag them out of the vault. But if I did, what then? They would only perish in the street, and here they were at least protected from the rain; and more than that, might die in seclusion.

I crawled up into the street. Looking down upon them again, I almost repented that I had brought them any food; for it would only prolong their misery, without hope of any permanent relief: for die they must very soon; they were too far gone for any medicine to help them. I hardly know whether I ought to confess another thing that occurred to me as I stood there; but it was this — I felt an almost irresistible impulse to do them the last mercy, of in some way putting an end to their horrible lives. I should almost have done so, I think, had I not been prevented by thoughts of the law. For I well knew that the law, which would let them perish of themselves without giving them one cup of water, would spend a thousand pounds, if necessary, in convicting him who should so much as offer to relieve them from their miserable existence.

The next day, and the next, I passed the vault three times, and still met the same sight: the girls leaning up against the woman on each side, and the woman with her arms still folding the babe, and her head bowed. The first evening I did not see the bread that I had dropped down in the morning; but the second evening, the bread I had dropped that morning remained untouched. On the third morning the smell that came from the vault was such that I accosted the same policeman I had accosted before, who was patrolling the same street, and told him that the persons I had spoken to him about were

"It's none of my business, Jack."

dead, and he had better have them removed. He looked as if he did
not believe me, and added that it was not his street.

When I arrived at the docks on my way to the ship, I entered the
guardhouse within the walls, and asked for one of the captains. I
told him the story. But from what he said, I was led to believe that
the Dock Police was distinct from that of the town, and this was not
the right place to lodge my information.

I could do no more that morning, being obliged to return to the
ship. At 12 o'clock, when I went to dinner, I hurried into Launcelott's-Hey, when I found that the vault was empty. In place of the
women and children, a heap of quick-lime[9] was glistening.

I could not learn who had taken them away, or where they had
gone; but my prayer was answered — they were dead, departed, and
at peace.

But again I looked down into the vault and in fancy beheld the
pale, shrunken forms still crouching there. Ah! what are our creeds,
and how do we hope to be saved? Tell me, oh Bible, that story of
Lazarus again, that I may find comfort in my heart for the poor and
forlorn.[10] Surrounded as we are by the wants and woes of our
fellowmen, and yet given to follow our own pleasures, regardless of

their pains, are we not like people sitting up with a corpse, and making merry in the house of the dead?

[1] **squalor:** filth caused by poverty or neglect
[2] **livid:** pale; ashen ·
[3] **unimploring:** not begging or pleading
[4] **gall:** bile; bitterness
[5] **obtrude:** thrust oneself upon others
[6] **victuals:** food
[7] **convulsively:** with contractions of the muscles
[8] **indigo:** a plant that produces a blue dye
[9] **quick-lime:** a dry white powder used to keep disease from spreading
[10] **forlorn:** miserable; wretched

A CLOSER LOOK

1. Whom does Redburn ask for help? What are their reasons for not helping? Why can't he do more for them himself?

2. What sort of person is Redburn? What makes him behave as he does?

3. Whom does Redburn blame for the fate of this unfortunate family? Who do you think was to blame? Could something like this happen today in our society? Why or why not?

• How important are political issues in the face of death? Walking past a cemetery, Langston Hughes considered this question. Then he wrote about it in this haunting poem.

Langston Hughes

PEACE

We passed their graves:
The dead men there,
Winners or losers,
Did not care.

In the dark
They could not see
Who had gained
The victory.

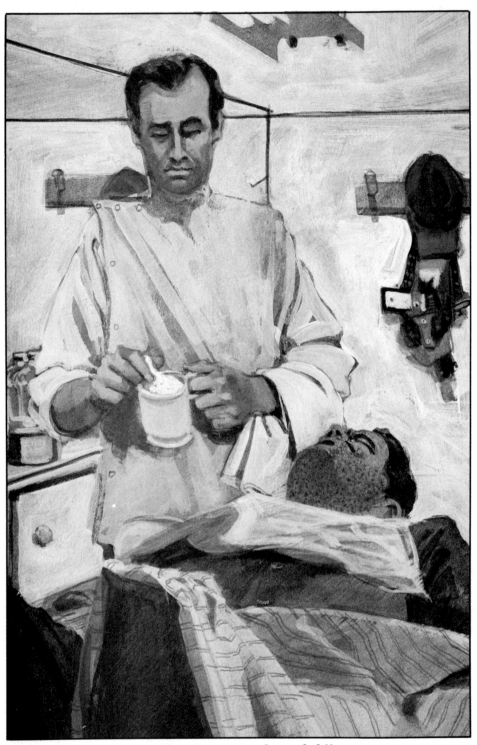

"Yes, I was secretly a rebel."

Hernando Téllez

JUST LATHER, THAT'S ALL

• Many nations have been torn by civil war. When countrymen fight against each other, it is often difficult to know who is your ally and who is your enemy. In such situations, people must cling tightly to their beliefs in order to find the best way to act.

HE SAID NOTHING WHEN HE ENTERED. I WAS passing the best of my razors back and forth on a strop.[1] When I recognized him I started to tremble. But he didn't notice. Hoping to conceal my emotion, I continued sharpening the razor. I tested it on the meat of my thumb, and then held it up to the light. At that moment he took off the bullet-studded belt that his gun holster dangled from. He hung it up on a wall hook and placed his military cap over it. Then he turned to me, loosening the knot of his tie, and said, "It's unbearably hot. Give me a shave." He sat in the chair.

I estimated he had a four-day beard. These were the four days taken up by the latest expedition in search of our troops. His face seemed reddened, burned by the sun. Carefully, I began to prepare the soap. I cut off a few slices, dropped them into the cup, mixed in a bit of warm water, and began to stir with the brush. Immediately the foam began to rise. "The other boys in the group should have this much beard, too," he said. I continued stirring the lather.

"But we did all right, you know. We got the main ones. We

brought back some dead, and we've got some others still alive. But pretty soon they'll all be dead.''

"How many did you catch?" I asked.

"Fourteen. We had to go pretty deep into the woods to find them. But we'll get even. Not one of them comes out of this alive, not one." He leaned back on the chair when he saw me with the lather-covered brush in my hand. I still had to put the sheet on him. No doubt about it, I was upset. I took a sheet out of a drawer and knotted it around my customer's neck. He wouldn't stop talking. He probably thought I was in sympathy with his party.

"The town must have learned a lesson from what we did the other day," he said.

"Yes," I replied, securing the knot at his dark, sweaty neck.

"That was a fine show, eh?"

"Very good," I answered, turning back for the brush. The man closed his eyes with a gesture of fatigue and sat waiting for the cool caress of the soap. I had never had him so close to me. The day he ordered the whole town to file into the patio of the school to see the four rebels hanging there, I came face-to-face with him for an instant. But the sight of the mutilated[2] bodies kept me from noticing the face of the man who had directed it all, the face I was now about to take into my hands. It was not an unpleasant face, certainly. And the beard, which made him seem a bit older than he was, didn't suit him badly at all. His name was Torres. Captain Torres. A man of imagination, because who else would have thought of hanging the naked rebels and then holding target practice on their bodies?

I began to apply the first layer of soap. With his eyes closed, he continued. "Without any effort I could go straight to sleep," he said, "but there's plenty to do this afternoon." I stopped the lathering and asked with a feigned[3] lack of interest: "A firing squad?" "Something like that, but a little slower." I got on with the job of lathering his beard. My hands started trembling again. The man could not possibly realize it, and this was in my favor. But I would have preferred that he hadn't come. It was likely that many of our faction had seen him enter. And an enemy under one's roof imposes certain conditions. I would be obliged to shave that beard like any other one, carefully, gently, like that of any customer, taking pains to see that no single pore emitted a drop of blood. I had to be careful that the little tufts of hair did not lead the blade astray. I had to see that his skin ended up clean, soft, and healthy, so that

110

passing the back of my hand over it I couldn't feel a hair. Yes, I was secretly a rebel, but I was also a conscientious barber, and proud of the preciseness of my profession. And this four days' growth of beard was a fitting challenge.

I took the razor, opened up the two protective arms, exposed the blade, and began the job, from one of the sideburns downward. The razor responded beautifully. His beard was inflexible[4] and hard, not too long, but thick. Bit by bit the skin emerged. The razor rasped along, making its customary sound as fluffs of lather mixed with bits of hair gathered along the blade. I paused a moment to clean it, then took up the strop again to sharpen the razor, because I'm a barber who does things properly. The man, who had kept his eyes closed, opened them now, removed one of his hands from under the sheet, felt the spot on his face where the soap had been cleared off, and said, "Come to the school today at six o'clock." " The same thing as the other day?" I asked, horrified. "It could be better," he replied. "What do you plan to do?" "I don't know yet. But we'll amuse ourselves." Once more he leaned back and closed his eyes. I approached him with the razor poised. "Do you plan to punish them all?" I ventured[5] timidly.

"All."

The soap was drying on his face. I had to hurry. In the mirror I looked toward the street. It was the same as ever: the grocery store with two or three customers in it. Then I glanced at the clock: two-twenty in the afternoon. The razor continued on its downward stroke. Now from the other sideburn down. He had a thick, blue beard. He should have let it grow like some poets or priests do. It would suit him well. A lot of people wouldn't recognize him. That would be much to his benefit, I thought, as I attempted to cover the neck area smoothly. There, for sure, the razor had to be handled masterfully, since the hair, although softer, grew into little swirls. He had a curly beard. One of the tiny pores could be opened up and issue forth its pearl of blood. A good barber such as I prides himself on never allowing this to happen to a client. And this was a first-class client. How many of us had he ordered shot? How many of us had he ordered mutilated? It was better not to think about it. Torres did not know that I was his enemy. He did not know it nor did the rest. It was a secret shared by very few, precisely so that I could inform the revolutionaries of what Torres was doing in the town and of what he was planning each time he undertook a rebel-hunting excursion. So it was going to be very difficult to explain that I had him right in my hands and let him go peacefully — alive and shaved.

The beard was now almost completely gone. He seemed younger, less burdened by years than when he had arrived. I suppose this always happens with men who visit barbershops. Under the stroke of my razor, Torres was being rejuvenated[6] — rejuvenated because I am a good barber, the best in the town, if I may say so. I dab a little more lather here, under his chin, on his Adam's apple, on this big vein. How hot it is getting! Torres must be sweating as much as I. But he is not afraid. He is a calm man, who is not even thinking about what he is going to do with the prisoners this afternoon. On the other hand, I, with this razor in my hand, stroking and restroking this skin, trying to keep blood from oozing from these pores, can't even think clearly. Curse him for coming, because I'm a revolutionary and not a murderer. And how easy it would be to kill him. And he deserves it. Does he? No! What the devil! No one deserves to have someone else make the sacrifice of becoming a murderer. What do you gain by it? Nothing. Others come along and still others, and the first ones kill the second ones, and they the next ones, and it goes on like this until everything is a sea of blood. I could cut this throat just so, zip! zip! I wouldn't give him time to complain, and since he has his eyes closed he wouldn't see the glistening knife blade or my glistening eyes. But I'm trembling like a real murderer. Out of his neck a gush of blood would spout onto the sheet, on the chair, on my hands, on the floor. I would have to close the door. And the blood would keep inching along the floor, warm, ineradicable,[7] uncontainable, until it reached the street, like a little scarlet stream. I'm sure that one solid stroke, one deep incision would prevent any pain. He wouldn't suffer. But what would I do with the body? Where would I hide it? I would have to flee, leaving all I have behind, and take refuge far away, far, far away. But they would follow until they found me. "Captain Torres' murderer. He slit his throat while he was shaving him — a coward." And then on the other side: "The avenger of us all. A name to remember. (And here they would mention my name.) He was the town barber. No one knew he was defending our cause."

And what of all this? Murderer or hero? My destiny depends on the edge of this blade. I can turn my hand a bit more, press a little harder on the razor, and sink it in. The skin would give way like

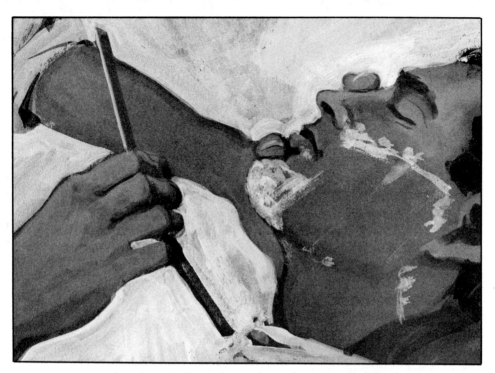

"My destiny depends on the edge of this blade."

silk, like rubber, like the strop. There is nothing more tender than human skin and the blood is always there, ready to pour forth. A blade like this doesn't fail. It is my best. But I don't want to be a murderer, no sir. You came to me for a shave. And I perform my work honorably. . . . I don't want blood on my hands. Just lather, that's all. You are an executioner and I am only a barber. Each person has his own place in the scheme of things. That's right. His own place.

Now his chin had been stroked clean and smooth. The man sat up and looked into the mirror. He rubbed his hands over his skin and felt it fresh, like new.

"Thanks," he said. He went to the hanger for his belt, pistol, and cap. I must have been very pale; my shirt felt soaked. Torres finished adjusting the buckle, and straightened his pistol in the holster. After automatically smoothing down his hair, he put on the cap. From his pants pocket he took out several coins to pay me for my services. And he began to head toward the door. In the doorway he paused for a moment, and turning to me he said:

"They told me that you'd kill me. I came to find out. But killing isn't easy. You can take my word for it.'' And he headed on down the street.

[1] **strop:** a leather strap which barbers use to sharpen their razors
[2] **mutilated:** crippled; suffered the loss of limbs
[3] **feigned:** pretended; faked
[4] **inflexible:** stiff; firm
[5] **ventured:** risked asking
[6] **rejuvenated:** given back one's youthful qualities
[7] **ineradicable:** that which can't be erased or cleaned up

A CLOSER LOOK

1. Who is the man in the barber chair? What is his job? How does the barber feel about this man?

2. How close does the barber really come to killing the captain? What holds him back? What is most important to the barber: his personal feelings, his professional responsiblities, or his political cause? Explain your answer.

3. What are the barber's strengths or good qualities? What good qualities does the captain possess? Which man do you admire more? Why?

● In this poem, Southern author Wendell Berry carries on an imaginary conversation with a rural man, like himself, who just happens to live in the Soviet Union. Although their two countries are often in conflict, must the two men be conflict with each other, too?

Wendell Berry

TO A SIBERIAN¹ WOODSMAN
(after looking at some pictures in a magazine)

1.

You lean at ease in your warm house at night after supper,
listening to your daughter play the accordion. You smile
with the pleasure of a man confident in his hands, resting
after a day of long labor in the forest, the cry of the saw
in your head, and the vision of coming home to rest.
Your daughter's face is clear in the joy of hearing
her own music. Her fingers live on the keys
like people familiar with the land they were born in.

You sit at the dinner table late into the night with your son,
tying the bright flies that will lead you along the forest
    streams.
Over you, as your hands work, is the dream of the still pools.
    Over you is the dream
of your silence while the east brightens, birds waking close
    by you in the trees.

2.

I have thought of you stepping out of your doorway at dawn,
    your son in your tracks.

115

You go in under the overarching green branches of the forest
whose ways, strange to me, are well known to you as the
sound of your own voice
or the silence that lies around you now that you have ceased
to speak,
and soon the voice of the stream rises ahead of you, and you
take the path beside it.
I have thought of the sun breaking pale through the mists
over you
as you come to the pool where you will fish, and of the mist
drifting
over the water, and of the cast fly resting light on the face
of the pool.

3.

And I am here in Kentucky in the place I have made myself
in the world. I sit on my porch above the river that flows
muddy
and slow along the feet of the trees. I hear the voice of the
wren
and the yellow-throated warbler whose songs pass near the
windows
and over the roof. In my house my daughter learns the
womanhood
of her mother. My son is at play, pretending to be
the man he believes I am. I am the outbreathing of this
ground.
My words are its words as the wren's song is its song.

4.

Who has invented our enmity?[2] Who has prescribed[3] us
hatred of each other? Who has armed us against each other
with the death of the world? Who has appointed me such
anger
that I should desire the burning of your house or the
destruction of your children?
Who has appointed such anger to you? Who has set loose
the thought
that we should oppose each other with the ruin of forests

and rivers, and the silence of birds?

Who has said to us that the voices of my land shall be strange
to you, and the voices of your land strange to me?

Who has imagined that I would destroy myself in order to
destroy you,

or that I could improve myself by destroying you? Who has
imagined

that your death could be negligible[4] to me now that I have
seen these pictures of your face?

Who has imagined that I would not speak familiarly with
you,

or laugh with you, or visit in your house and go to work with
you in the forest?

And now one of the ideas of my place will be that you would
gladly talk and visit and work with me.

5.

I sit in the shade of the trees of the land I was born in.

As they are native I am native, and I hold to this place as
carefully as they hold to it.

I do not see the national flag flying from the staff of the
sycamore,

or any decree of the government written on the leaves of the
walnut,

nor has the elm bowed before monuments or sworn the oath
of allegiance.

They have not declared to whom they stand in welcome.

6.

In the thought of you I imagine myself free of the weapons
and the official hates that I have borne[5] on my back
like a hump,

and in the thought of myself I imagine you free of weapons
and official hates,

so that if we should meet we would not go by each other
looking at the ground like slaves sullen[6] under their
burdens,

but would stand clear in the gaze of each other.

7.

There is no government so worthy as your son who fishes
　　with you in silence beside the forest pool.

There is no national glory so comely[7] as your daughter whose
　　hands have learned a music and go their own way on
　　the keys.

There is no national glory so comely as my daughter who
　　dances and sings and is the brightness of my house.

There is no government so worthy as my son who laughs, as
　　he comes up the path from the river in the evening,
　　for joy.

[1] **Siberian:** a person from a region in the eastern part of the Soviet Union
[2] **enmity:** hatred
[3] **prescribed:** ordered
[4] **negligible:** of little importance
[5] **borne:** carried
[6] **sullen:** gloomy
[7] **comely:** pleasant; fit

A CLOSER LOOK

*1. What things does Berry refer to in the Russian family's life
that are similar to things in his own life?*

*2. Look at the passage where Berry asks a series of "Who"
questions. Try to give an answer to each of these questions.*

*3. What is Berry's idea for solving national differences? Do you
think it would work?*

● One way to get your thoughts and feelings sorted out is to keep a journal, as Henry Thoreau did (see page 57). In his journal, Hugh Prather wrote down his ideas about many aspects of life. He eventually published this book so that readers could share and perhaps learn from his thoughts and feelings.

Hugh Prather

NOTES TO MYSELF: VALUES

Now that I know I'm no wiser than anyone else, does this wisdom make me wiser?

Sometimes the only way for me to find out what it is I want to do is to go ahead and do something. Then the moment I start to act, my feelings become clear.

My saying "and" and "uh" results from my need to answer immediately, to speak without any break, as if taking time to think were embarrassing.

I walk down the street and the guy waiting for the bus — who has been waiting there for who knows how long — suddenly finds something more interesting to look at than a live human being. I do the same. Do I avoid looking a stranger in the eyes because I don't want to make him uncomfortable, or do I turn my eyes so he can't look into me? What is there in me that I don't want him to see?

A CLOSER LOOK

1. Judging from these few statements, what kind of a man would you expect Prather to be?

2. What is the difference between expressing your thoughts as Prather does here, and expressing them in essay form?

3. Which of these statements is most interesting to you? Explain why.

● Lewis Thomas (see page 35) has shown us that lying takes its toll on the human body. Now one of Nigeria's leading contemporary poets describes the toll it may take on the human soul. Okara is not speaking of huge, deliberate falsehoods — only of the "tiny" lies he sees and hears every day in society.

Gabriel Okara

ONCE UPON A TIME

Once upon a time, son,
they used to laugh with their hearts
and laugh with their eyes;
but now they only laugh with their teeth,
while their ice-block-cold eyes
search behind my shadow.

There was a time indeed
they used to shake hands with their hearts;
but that's gone, son.
Now they shake hands without hearts
while their left hands search
my empty pockets.

So I have learned many things, son.
I have learned to wear many faces
like dresses — homeface,
officeface, streetface, hostface, cocktail-
face, with all their conforming smiles
like a fixed portrait smile.

And I have learned too
to laugh with only my teeth
and shake hands without my heart.
I have also learned to say "Goodbye,"
when I mean "Goodriddance";
to say "Glad to meet you,"
without being glad; and to say, "It's been
nice talking to you," after being bored.

But believe me, son,
I want to be what I used to be
when I was like you. I want
to unlearn all these muting things.
Most of all, I want to relearn
how to laugh, for my laugh in the mirror
shows only my teeth like a snake's bare fangs!

So show me, son,
how to laugh; show me how
I used to laugh and smile
once upon a time when I was like you.

"Go, trashman, go!"

John Coleman

THE TRASHMAN

● When John Coleman wrote this journal he was president of
Haverford College in Pennsylvania and chairman of the board of the
Federal Reserve Bank in Philadelphia. Upset by the lack of
communication between the academic and the working
communities in America, and eager to vary the rhythm of his life, he
took an unusual two-month leave of absence and went to work as
a garbage collector in a Washington, DC , suburb.

SATURDAY, APRIL 7

STEVE AND I HAULED TRASH FOR A SOLID FOUR
hours without a break of any sort, except for about five
minutes when we stopped to talk. We got eight hours of
pay for cleaning up our route regardless of how little time it
took. If we moved slowly, we hurt only ourselves.

My shoulder called out for mercy each time I put another full
barrel on it, and my legs occasionally shook as I started out to the
street. But all the rest of me said, "Go, trashman, go."

I could not have guessed that there would be joy in this. Dump.
Lift. Walk. Lift. Walk. The hours went by quickly.

Saturday meant that most adults were at home on the route. So
were school-age children. I thought this might mean more talk back
and forth as I made the rounds today. There were many people
outdoors, tending to their spring yard chores. Most of them looked
friendly enough. While I wouldn't have time to talk at length, there
was time to exchange the greetings that go with civilized ways.

That is where I got my shock.

I said hello in quite a few yards before the message sank in that this wasn't the thing to do. Occasionally, I got a straight man-to-man or woman-to-woman reply from someone who looked me in the eye, smiled, and asked either "How are you?" or "Isn't this a nice day?" I felt human then. But most often the response was either nothing at all, a look of surprise that I had spoken and used a familiar tongue, or an overly sweet hello.

Both men and women gave me the silent or staring treatment. A woman in housecoat and curlers was startled as I came around the corner of her house. At the sound of my greeting, she gathered her housecoat tightly about her and moved quickly indoors. I heard the lock click. Another woman had a strange, large animal in her yard. I asked her what kind of dog it was. She gaped at me. I thought she was hard of hearing and asked my question louder. There was a touch of a shudder before she turned coldly away.

The sweet treatment came from women alone. From the way they replied and asked after my health, I knew that at the day's end when they listed the nice things they had done, there would be a place on the list for "I spoke to the trashman today."

I shouldn't have been so caught by surprise. I had read Robert Coles' *The South Goes North* and had been moved by his interview with a Boston garbage collector who said: "I could see the ten- or twelve-year-old kids do one of three things: they'd snicker, or they'd look at you as though you're a freak or something, or they'd feel sorry for you." But reading those things was different from having them happen to me.

Steve spoke spontaneously about these things on the long ride to the dump.

"The way most people look at you, you'd think a trashman was a monster. Say hello and they stare at you in surprise. They don't know we're human.

"This one lady put cinder blocks in her can. I said we couldn't take them. She said, 'Who are you to say what goes? You're nothing but a trashman.' I told her, 'Listen, lady, I got an I.Q. of 137, and I graduated near the top of my high school class. I do this for the money, not because it's all I can do.'

"I want to tell them, 'Look, I come as clean as you do,' but it wouldn't help. I don't tell anyone I'm a trashman. I say I'm a truck driver. My family knows, but my in-laws don't. If someone comes right out and asks, 'Do you drive for a trash company?' I say yes. I figure we're doing a service that people need, like a police officer or a fire fighter. I'm not ashamed of it, but I don't go around boasting about it either.

"A friend of my wife yelled at her kid one day when they were running out to meet a trash truck. 'Stay away from those trashmen. They're dirty.' I blew up at her. 'They're as good as we are,' I told her. 'You seem to have a lot of sympathy for them,' she said. 'Yes, I do.' But I never told her why.

"I wish they'd change the name of the company. 'Liberty Refuse' sure doesn't help when you have to list your employer somewhere. When I rented an apartment, I changed the name on the application to 'Liberty Trucking Company.' I doubt if they would have rented to me if they knew I was a trashman."

I noticed that, while other employees had their first names above the left pockets of their blue work shirts and the company's name on a patch on the right, Steve had just his own name on his shirt. On the right side was a less faded area where a patch had been before.

Our truck was packed full before noon. We made the run to the dump, were back on the route by 1:00, and had finished for the day by 2:00.

I had planned to stay at this job for only two days. But now I'm going to stay. The exercise is great. The lifting gets easier with every load, even if my left shoulder stays sore. I become faster and neater as time goes by. I'm outdoors in clean air. And, contrary to what people think, I don't get dirty on the job.

I'm resolved, too, to go on saying hello in backyards. It can't hurt, and it still feels right. Frankly, I'm proud. I'm doing an essential task, "like a police officer or a fire fighter." I left this country a little cleaner than I found it this morning. Not many people can say that tonight.

THURSDAY, APRIL 12

I've been interested in watching for the defenses which trashmen build against those who look down on them. I have met men this week who simply close up into themselves once they are on the route, get the job done, and get out of those neighborhoods as fast as they can. I doubt that they even return a greeting in the few cases where a householder extends that courtesy first.

I have listened, too, to those among us who go that extra mile in asserting pride in themselves. One man spoke of how insulted he was by the woman who said, perhaps with only kindly intent, "Those dresses in the can aren't really very old. Wouldn't you like to take them to your wife?"

I saw pride asserted in a different way today. Steve had never spoken to me about how I was to leave the area around the cans where I dumped. But he made his point more effectively than any lecture could do. He showed me a photo that a housewife had given him of the mess left by one of his helpers; his anger that one of his men would do the job that badly was plain to see. He has been on this route eighteen months and knows how the job should be done.

I have no idea how many Steves there are on garbage routes today. The one I know may not stay there much longer. He talks either of studying accounting some day or of driving an over-the-road trailer truck. Maybe neither of those dreams will come true. But he is likely to do something where he gets as much credit as he gives.

John Gardner has said that a society which praises its philosophers and scorns its plumbers is in for trouble. "Neither its pipes nor its theories will hold water," he warns. He might have gone a step further and called for respect for both our economists and our refuse men; otherwise they'll both leave trash behind.

A CLOSER LOOK

1. Why do you think Dr. Coleman went to work as a garbage collector? What did he like about his new job? What didn't he like about his new job?

2. According to Dr. Coleman, how do most people treat garbage collectors? Why do you think that people behave this way?

3. What did Dr. Coleman learn from his experience? Do you think his experience could help him be a better banker or a better college president? Explain why or why not.

128

Russell G. Davis
and Brent K. Ashabranner

THE GIFT AND THE GIVER

● Folk tales are often moral lessons in disguise. Here's an African folk tale with a universal message about the art of giving.

ONCE A POOR FARMER FOUND A BEAUTIFUL apple growing on a tree in his fields. The apple was so large, so shiny, and so well shaped that the farmer cried with joy when he saw it. Never had he seen such a beautiful apple on any tree in his country.

The farmer picked the apple and wrapped it in his cloak and brought it to his home. He showed it to his wife and children, and they were as amazed as he was to see such a beautiful apple.

Other farmers who lived in that village heard of the apple and came to the house to see it. They, too, agreed that it was a wondrous apple. Farmers from distant villages came to see the fruit. They touched it tenderly and exclaimed in loud voices that it was a wonderful apple, shaped to perfection by the hand of God.

After all had admired the apple, the question came — what to do with it? The farmer wished to give it to his favorite daughter. He said to her, "Truly, this is the only thing that matches you in beauty. On both the fruit and your fair face, the work of God's hand is clear. Take it and eat of it, my beauty."

"A gift is only as good as the heart of the giver."

But the daughter was too modest. She said she was not worthy of such a thing. She urged her father to take the fruit for himself. It was given to him as a sign of God's love and blessings. "It is worthy of a king," the daughter said.

"You are right," the farmer agreed. "Why didn't I think of that myself? Such a fruit *is* worthy of a king. I will take it to the King. It is the only gift that I, a poor farmer, can give that will be worthy of my King."

The farmer's wife wrapped the apple in the finest cloth she had, and the farmer set out for the royal city. The farmer carried the fruit very carefully in the cloth, and he walked along the road slowly. After many days, he reached the city, but the poor farmer could not get in to see the King. The guards at the palace laughed at him and kept him out.

"The King has thousands of fruit trees," they said. "Surely your fruit can be no more beautiful than that of the King."

The farmer opened the cloth and asked the guards to look. The apple was still as beautiful as the day it had been picked. The farmer would not let any of the guards touch the fruit. Finally they went away to call the commander. The commander admired the apple greatly, although the farmer would not let him touch it. The commander of the guard decided that he would bring the farmer to the chambers of the King.

When the farmer came before the King, he spoke in this way: "Your Majesty, great King, beloved of all of us. I found a most beautiful apple on one of the trees in my field. It was such a wondrously beautiful fruit that men came from miles around to see it. I decided that only our beloved King could deserve such a thing. So I have carried the fruit a great distance from my house. And I wish to give it to you."

The King was greatly moved by the simple love of the farmer. "What would you have in return?" the King asked. "Name it, and it is yours."

The farmer was surprised. "I want nothing but to see the joy on your face when you see this that God has made."

The farmer opened his cloth and showed the fruit to the King. "It is surely a work of God's hand," the King agreed. "Such size! Such color! Such a shine! It shines like a bright jewel."

The King called the Queen and all of the family, and they, too, marveled at the beautiful apple. While the people of the palace were admiring the apple, the poor farmer left the court and started for his home. The King noticed this.

"Where is the farmer?" he asked. "He has shown me more love with this gift than anyone in my kingdom. Ride after him. Take my best horse and give it to him. Tell him the horse is from a grateful king who has learned a new lesson in kindness."

The servants rode after the farmer and found him plodding along the road. The farmer was very happy with the gift, which he had not expected. He rode away toward his village.

Word travels fast in a palace. Soon all the people in the royal city learned that the King had given his best horse to a poor farmer — and in exchange for a mere piece of fruit.

A rich merchant of the town heard the story of the King's gift. The merchant began to scheme. He thought, "That poor farmer gave the King a simple apple from a tree. And the King gave him his best horse in exchange. What would the King give me if I gave him a horse? He might give me his daughter. Or perhaps some valuable jewels!"

The merchant picked the finest horse from his stable and led it up to the gates of the palace. "I have a gift for the King," the merchant told the guards. The guards let the rich merchant in at once.

The merchant went before the King. "I have heard that you have given your own horse to a farmer," the merchant said. "For that reason, I have brought you a fine horse from my stable."

"Thank you very much," the King said.

The merchant moved restlessly, first standing on one foot and then the other. The merchant stroked his beard and looked worried. "Did you want something of me?" the King asked. The merchant stared down at the floor and did not meet the King's eyes.

"Ah, I see," the King said. "You have given me a gift. Now you expect something in return. Very well. Wait right here."

The King left the room. The merchant could hardly hide his joy. "It will be the jewels," he thought. "He has gone to get the jewels. I'm sure it will be the jewels."

The King returned carrying something wrapped in a rich cloth. "Take this apple," the King said. "It is most precious to me because it was given by a man who expected nothing in return. But you may have it."

The rich merchant was stunned. When he opened up the cloth he saw the perfection of the apple, but he paid no attention to its beauty. The merchant walked angrily out of the palace. When he was outside, he threw away the fruit. He began to pull out his beard and wail in a loud voice.

The King ordered his guards to drive the merchant from the palace grounds. "Tell him," the King said, "that a gift is only as good as the heart of the giver. A person should give without expecting a gift in return. Any other gift is worthless."

The King looked at the beautiful horse the merchant had brought him. "The merchant's horse is worthless as a gift," the King said. "As something to ride on, however, it seems to be a very fine horse."

A CLOSER LOOK

1. Why did the farmer give his apple to the King? Why did the King accept it?

2. Why did the King give the apple to the merchant? Do you think he knew how the merchant would respond?

3. What is the moral of this folk tale? Do you agree with this moral? Explain why or why not.

"As soon as the bell rang . . . the virus attacked."

Art Buchwald

SCHOLASTIS ADOLESCUM

● A syndicated columnist pokes fun at a strange illness that plagues students through all their years in school. You may have your own name for this mysterious disease.

I N THE ANNALS OF MEDICAL SCIENCE, NO VIRUS HAS given doctors as much trouble as the *Scholastis Adolescum*, otherwise known as school sickness.

The *Scholastis Adolescum* has been known to attack children of all ages and on every economic and social level. The symptoms are always the same. The child wakes up in the morning and says he has a "pain in the stomach," a "headache," a "sore throat" or he "just doesn't feel well." In rare cases the child may also have a "slight" fever.

What has puzzled scientists for years is that the virus only attacks on weekdays and never on weekends or during summer vacations. It lasts only twenty-four hours, and while it has no serious aftereffects, it keeps returning during the school year and even builds up in intensity just before test time.

Very little was know about the *Scholastis Adolescum* until Professor Heinrich Applebaum, in charge of virology[1] at the Dropout Institute of Technology, did some unbelievable experiments in his laboratory.

Professor Applebaum used white mice for his experiment. He built a large cage with a tiny schoolhouse with tiny classrooms. In the back was a play yard with swings, ropes, and colored tubes to play in. On top of the schoolhouse was a tiny bell. When Professor Applebaum rang the bell once, that meant the mice had to go to "school." When he rang twice, school was "out" and the mice could play.

At first Professor Applebaum let the mice play in the schoolyard. They were chipper and frisky, and jumped all over one another. Then he rang the school bell. As soon as the bell rang, indicating that class was ready to start, the virus attacked and the mice became sluggish[2] and ill-tempered. They pushed and shoved into the schoolhouse. Some held their stomachs as if they had an ache. Others started coughing fits, and still others rolled over on their backs, pretending they couldn't move.

After two hours Professor Applebaum rang the bell again, indicating that school was out and it was playtime. The ailing mice suddenly came alive. All their symptoms seemed to disappear, and they were their old selves again.

Encouraged, the professor tried a further experiment. He assigned the mice "homework," such as putting tiny pieces of wood into a box or sticking shreds of paper in a row. Once again the virus struck, and the mice complained of headaches, nausea, and, in two cases, of toothaches.

Professor Applebaum then placed a television set in front of the mice and turned it on. The mice immediately rushed toward the set, jumping up and down in joy. They seemed to forget their aches and pains and sat entranced. All fatigue disappeared, and they refused to go to bed, even though a few hours previously they could hardly sit up.

In his final experiment, Professor Applebaum announced that he would give the mice a "test" on the following morning, and told them all to study.

The next morning when the professor came into his laboratory he found every mouse, without exception, on his back with his feet in the air. The virus had struck again!

He then called off the test, and the mice rolled over and started playing happily in the school playground.

On the basis of these experiments Professor Applebaum concluded that the *Scholastis Adolescum* was connected with the nervous system and would attack at any time the mice had to go to "school," do "homework," or face "tests." It would disappear only if the mice were assured they could play or watch television.

The mice in the experiment have by now all had offspring, and the offspring have all suffered from *Scholastis Adolescum*, showing conclusively that school sickness is inherited and passed on from one generation to another.

Doctors have taken Professor Applebaum's findings and are now trying to apply them to children. If a cure for *Scholastis Adolescum* can be found, millions of days of absenteeism can be saved, and one of the major health menaces in America can be licked.

[1] **virology:** the science that deals with viruses
[2] **sluggish:** slow-moving

A CLOSER LOOK

1. What is Scholastis Adolescum? *What causes it?*

2. What tests does Professor Applebaum perform? What do these tests prove?

3. How would you cure someone of Scholastis Adolescum? Do you think Buchwald's essay is funny? Explain why or why not.

"She was a real find."

I. B. Singer

THE WASHWOMAN

● Singer's childhood was spent in Warsaw, Poland, in the unique culture of a Jewish ghetto. Like many of his short stories, this one is drawn from a human drama he witnessed in his youth. Singer was the son of a rabbi, a religious leader of his community, and he pondered on such dramas, trying to understand what made each person behave in a certain way. His characters may behave like ordinary people, but he quietly makes you see that each one is a hero.

OUR HOME HAD LITTLE CONTACT WITH Gentiles.[1] The only Gentile in the building was the janitor. Fridays he would come for a tip, his ''Friday money.'' He remained standing at the door, took off his hat, and my mother gave him six groschen.

Besides the janitor there were also the Gentile washwomen who came to the house to fetch our laundry. My story is about one of these.

She was a small woman, old and wrinkled. When she started washing for us, she was already past seventy. Most Jewish women of her age were sickly, weak, broken in body. All the old women in our street had bent backs and leaned on sticks when they walked. But this washwoman, small and thin as she was, possessed a strength that came from generations of peasant forebears.[2] Mother would count out to her a bundle of laundry that had accumulated over several weeks. She would lift the unwieldy[3] pack, load it on her narrow shoulders, and carry it the long way home. She lived on Krochmalna Street, too, but at the other end, near the Wola section.

139

"She was a small woman, old and wrinkled."

It must have been a walk of an hour and a half.

She would bring the laundry back about two weeks later. My mother had never been so pleased with any washwoman. Every piece of linen sparkled like polished silver. Every piece was neatly ironed. Yet she charged no more than the others. She was a real find. Mother always had her money ready, because it was too far for the old woman to come a second time.

Laundering was not easy in those days. The old woman had no faucet where she lived, but had to bring in the water from a pump. For the linens to come out so clean, they had to be scrubbed thoroughly in a washtub, rinsed with washing soda, soaked, boiled in an enormous pot, starched, then ironed. Every piece was handled ten times or more. And the drying! It could not be done outside because thieves would steal the laundry. The wrung-out wash had to be carried up to the attic and hung on clotheslines. In the winter it would become as brittle as glass and almost break when touched. And there was always a to-do with other housewives and washwomen who wanted the attic clotheslines for their own use. Only God knows all the old woman had to endure each time she did a wash!

She could have begged at the church door or entered a home for the penniless and aged. But there was in her a certain pride and love of labor with which many Gentiles have been blessed. The old woman did not want to become a burden, and so bore her burden.

The woman had a son who was rich. I no longer remember what sort of business he had. He was ashamed of his mother, the washwoman, and never came to see her. Nor did he ever give her a groschen. The old woman told this without rancor.[4] One day the son was married. It seemed that he had made a good match. The wedding took place in a church. The son had not invited the old mother to his wedding, but she went to the church and waited at the steps to see her son lead the "young lady" to the altar. . . .

The story of the faithless son left a deep impression on my mother. She talked about it for weeks and months. It was an insult not only to the old woman but to the entire institution of motherhood. Mother would argue, "Nu, does it pay to make sacrifices for children? The mother uses up her last strength, and he does not even know the meaning of loyalty."

And she would drop dark hints that she was not certain of her own children: Who knows what they would do some day? This, however, did not prevent her from dedicating her life to us. If there was any delicacy[5] in the house, she would put it aside for the children and invent all sorts of excuses and reasons why she herself did not want to taste it. . . .

That winter was a harsh one. The streets were in the grip of a bitter cold. No matter how much we heated our stove, the windows were covered with frostwork and decorated with icicles. The newspapers reported that people were dying of the cold. Coal became dear. The winter had become so severe that parents stopped sending children to cheder,[6] and even the Polish schools were closed.

On one such day the washwoman, now nearly eighty years old, came to our house. A good deal of laundry had accumulated during the past weeks. Mother gave her a pot of tea to warm herself, as well as some bread. The old woman sat on a kitchen chair trembling and shaking, and warmed her hands against the teapot. Her fingers were gnarled from work, and perhaps from arthritis, too. Her fingernails were strangely white. These hands spoke of the stubbornness of mankind, of the will to work not only as one's strength permits but beyond the limits of one's power. Mother counted and wrote down the list: men's undershirts, women's vests, long-legged drawers, bloomers, petticoats, shifts, featherbed covers, pillowcases, sheets, and the men's fringed garments. Yes, the Gentile woman washed these holy garments as well.

The bundle was big, bigger than usual. When the woman placed it on her shoulders, it covered her completely. At first she stayed, as though she were about to fall under the load. But an inner obstinacy[7] seemed to call out: No, you may not fall. A donkey may permit himself to fall under his burden, but not a human being, the crown of creation.

It was fearful to watch the old woman staggering out with the enormous pack, out into the frost, where the snow was dry as salt and the air was filled with dusty white whirlwinds, like goblins dancing in the cold. Would the old woman ever reach Wola?

She disappeared, and Mother sighed and prayed for her.

Usually the woman brought back the wash after two or, at most, three weeks. But three weeks passed, then four and five, and nothing was heard of the old woman. We remained without linens. The cold had become even more intense. The telephone wires were now as thick as ropes. The branches of the trees looked like glass. So much snow had fallen that the streets had become uneven. Sleds were able to glide down many streets as on the slopes of a hill. Kind-hearted people lit fires in the streets for vagrants to warm themselves and roast potatoes in, if they had any to roast.

For us the washwoman's absence was a catastrophe. We needed the laundry. We did not even know the woman's address. It seemed certain that she had collapsed, died. Mother declared she had had a premonition,[8] as the old woman left our house that last time, that we would never see our things again. She found some old torn shirts and washed and mended them. We mourned, both for the laundry and for the old, toil-worn woman who had grown close to us through the years she had served us so faithfully.

More than two months passed. The frost had subsided, and then a new frost had come, a new wave of cold. One evening, while Mother was sitting near the kerosene lamp mending a shirt, the door opened and a small puff of steam, followed by a gigantic bundle, entered the room. I ran toward the old woman and helped her unload her pack. She was even thinner now, more bent. Her face had become more gaunt.[9] Her head shook from side to side as though she were saying no. She could not utter a clear word, but mumbled something with her sunken mouth and pale lips.

After the old woman had recovered somewhat, she told us that she

"I do not want to be a burden on anyone!"

had been ill, very ill. Just what her illness was, I cannot remember. She had been so sick that someone called a doctor, and the doctor had sent for a priest. Someone had informed the son, and he had contributed money for a coffin and for the funeral. But the Almighty had not yet wanted to take this pain-racked soul to Himself. She began to feel better, she became well, and as soon as she was able to stand on her feet once more, she resumed her washing. Not just ours, but the wash of several other families, too.

"I could not rest easy in my bed because of the wash," the old woman explained. "The wash would not let me die."

"With the help of God you will live to be a hundred and twenty," said my mother, as a benedictum.[10]

"God forbid! What good would such a long life be? The work becomes harder and harder . . . my strength is leaving me. . . . I do not want to be a burden on anyone!" The old woman muttered and crossed herself, and raised her eyes toward heaven.

Fortunately there was some money in the house and Mother counted out what she owed. I had a strange feeling: the coins in the old woman's washed-out hands seemed to become as worn and clean and pious[11] as she herself was. She blew on the coins and tied them in a kerchief. Then she left, promising to return in a few weeks for a new load.

But she never came back. The wash she had returned was her last effort on this earth. She had been driven by an indomitable[12] will to return the property to its rightful owners, to fulfill the task she had undertaken.

And now at last her body, which had long been no more than a shard[13] supported only by the force of honesty and duty, had fallen. Her soul passed into those spheres where all holy souls meet, regardless of the roles they played on this earth, in whatever tongue, of whatever creed. I cannot imagine paradise without this Gentile washwoman. I cannot even conceive of a world where there is no reward for such effort.

[1] **Gentiles:** persons other than Jews
[2] **forebears:** ancestors
[3] **unwieldy:** not easily handled
[4] **rancor:** bitterness
[5] **delicacy:** candy; sweet
[6] **cheder:** an elementary religious school for Jews
[7] **obstinacy:** stubbornness
[8] **premonition:** warning in advance
[9] **gaunt:** thin and angular
[10] **benedictum:** blessing
[11] **pious:** religious
[12] **indomitable:** unconquerable
[13] **shard:** a small, brittle piece

A CLOSER LOOK

1. How many Gentiles does young Singer know? What does he think makes the Gentile washwoman different from other people he knows?

2. What makes this old woman's life hard? What makes it easier?

3. How did you feel when you read the scene in which the old woman returns with the laundry? Did you expect this to happen? Do you think it's realistic?

Mahatma Gandhi

FAITH ON TRIAL

● During India's fight for independence from Great Britain, Gandhi was perhaps the most powerful Indian political figure. People of all social classes and religions loved and trusted this modest yet persistent man. Sometimes he went to prison for his beliefs or fasted to the brink of death to win a political point. As this essay shows, he was willing to suffer for his beliefs — personal beliefs as well as political ones — because they were so important to him.

THOUGH I HAD A HOUSE IN GIRGAUM, GOD WOULD not let me settle down. Scarcely had I moved into my new house when my second son Manilal — who had already been through an acute attack of smallpox some years back — had a severe attack of typhoid, combined with pneumonia and signs of delirium[1] at night.

The doctor was called in. He said medicine would have little effect, but eggs and chicken broth might be given with profit.

Manilal was only ten years old. To consult his wishes was out of the question.

Being his guardian, I had to decide. I told the doctor that we were all vegetarians and that I could not possibly give either of the two things to my son. Would he therefore recommend something else?

"Your son's life is in danger," said the good doctor. "We could give him milk diluted with water, but that will not give him enough nourishment. As you know, I am called in by many Hindu families, and they do not object to anything I prescribe. I think you will be well advised not to be so hard on your son."

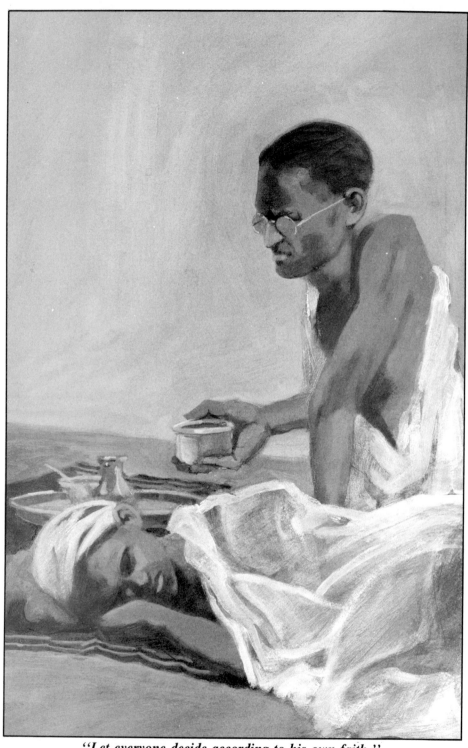

"Let everyone decide according to his own faith."

"What you say is quite right," said I. "As a doctor you could not do otherwise. But my responsibility is very great. If the boy had been grown up, I should certainly have tried to determine his wishes and respected them. But here I have to think and decide for him. To my mind it is only on such occasions that a man's faith is truly tested. Rightly or wrongly, it is part of my conviction that man may not eat meat, eggs, and the like. There should be a limit even to the means of keeping ourselves alive. Even for life itself we may not do certain things. Religion, as I understand it, does not permit me to use meat or eggs for me or my family, even on occasions like this. I must therefore take the risk you say is likely. But I beg of you one thing. As I cannot avail myself of your treatment, I propose to try some hydropathic remedies[2] which I happen to know. But I shall not know how to examine the boy's pulse, chest, lungs, etc. If you will kindly look in from time to time to examine him and keep me informed of his condition, I shall be grateful to you."

The good doctor appreciated my difficulty and agreed to my request. Though Manilal could not have made his choice, I told him what had passed between the doctor and myself and asked his opinion.

"Do try your hydropathic treatment," he said. "I will not have eggs or chicken broth."

This made me glad, though I realized that, if I had given him either of these, he would have taken it.

I knew Khune's hydropathic treatment and had tried it, too. I knew as well that fasting also could be tried with profit. So I began to give Manilal hip baths according to Khune, never keeping him in the tub for more than three minutes. I kept him on orange juice mixed with water for three days.

But the temperature persisted, going up to 104. At night he would be delirious. I began to get anxious. What would people say of me? What would my elder brother think of me? Could we not call in another doctor? What right had the parents to inflict their fads on their children?

I was haunted by thoughts like these. Then a contrary current would start. God would surely be pleased to see that I was giving the same treatment to my son as I would give myself. I had faith in hydropathy, and little faith in allopathy.[3] The doctors could not guarantee recovery. At best they could experiment. The thread of life was in the hands of God. Why not trust it to Him and in His name go on with what I thought was the right treatment?

My mind was torn between these conflicting thoughts. It was night. I was in Manilal's bed lying by his side. I decided to give him a wet sheet pack. I got up and wetted a sheet. I wrung the water out of it and wrapped it about Manilal, keeping only his head out. I then covered him with two blankets. To the head I applied a wet towel. The whole body was burning like hot iron, and quite parched. There was absolutely no perspiration.

I was sorely tired. I left Manilal in the charge of his mother, and went out for a walk on Chaupati to refresh myself. It was about ten o'clock. Very few pedestrians were out. Plunged in deep thought, I scarcely looked at them, "My honor is in Thy keeping, oh Lord, in this hour of trial," I repeated to myself. *Ramanama* was on my lips. After a short time I returned, my heart beating within my breast.

No sooner had I entered the room than Manilal said, "You have returned, Bapu?"

"Yes, darling."

"Do please pull me out. I am burning."

"Are you perspiring, my boy?"

"I am simply soaked. Do please take me out."

I felt his forehead. It was covered with beads of perspiration. The temperature was going down. I thanked God.

"Manilal, your fever is sure to go now. A little more perspiration and then I will take you out."

"Pray, no. Do deliver me from this furnace. Wrap me some other time if you like."

I just managed to keep him under the pack for a few minutes more by diverting him. The perspiration streamed down his forehead. I undid the pack and dried his body. Father and son fell asleep in the same bed.

And each slept like a log. Next morning Manilal had much less fever. He went on thus for forty days on diluted milk and fruit juices. I had no fear now. It was an obstinate type of fever, but it had been got under control.

Today Manilal is the healthiest of my boys. Who can say whether his recovery was due to God's grace, or to hydropathy, or to careful diet and nursing? Let everyone decide according to his own faith. For my part I was sure that God had saved my honor, and that belief remains unaltered to this day.

[1] **delirium:** fever accompanied by wild excitement, irrational talk, and hallucinations
[2] **hydropathic remedies:** the scientific use of water to treat disease
[3] **allopathy:** in effect, conventional or traditional medical practices

A CLOSER LOOK

1. Why did Gandhi find it impossible to follow the doctor's orders? What did he risk by not following them? What did he feel he would risk by following them?

2. How does Gandhi feel about his decision after he has made it? What does this tell you about his personality? What does this tell you about the strength of his beliefs?

3. Do you think Gandhi really loved his son? Give evidence from the text to support your opinion.

"They want to share in the American Dream."

Studs Terkel

AMERICAN DREAMS — LOST AND FOUND

● Like Robert Coles (see page 67), writer Studs Terkel records oral history. His subjects in this essay, however, are modern Americans across the country, some of them famous, some unknown. Speaking into Terkel's tape recorder, they confessed their hopes, disappointments, and dreams. Taken together, these conversations reveal a great deal about what seems important in our society — and what really is important.

EMMA KNIGHT

Miss U.S.A., 1973. She is twenty-nine.

I wince when I'm called a former beauty queen or Miss U.S.A. I keep thinking they're talking about someone else. For many girls who enter the contest, it's part of the American Dream. It was never mine.

We used to sit around the TV and watch Miss America, and it was exciting, we thought, glamorous. Fun, we thought. But by the time I was eight or nine, I didn't feel comfortable. Soon I'm hitting my adolescence, like fourteen, but I'm not doing any dating and I'm feeling awkward and ugly. I'm much taller than most of the people in my class. I don't feel I can compete the way I see girls competing for guys. I was very much of a loner. I felt intimidated[1] by the amount of competition females were supposed to go through with each other. I didn't like being told by *Seventeen* magazine: Forget your own interests. If you have a crush on a guy, get interested in what he's interested in. If you play cards, be sure not to beat him. I was very bad at these social games.

151

After I went to the University of Colorado for three and a half years, I had had it. This was 1968 through '71. I came home for the summer. An agent met me and wanted me to audition for commercials, modeling, acting jobs. Okay. I started auditioning and winning some.

I did things actors do when they're starting out. You pass out literature at conventions, you pound the pavements, you send out your resumés.[2] I went to a model agency one cold day, and an agent came out and said: "I want you to enter a beauty contest." I said: "No, uh-uh, never, never, never. I'll lose, how humiliating." She said: "I want some girls to represent the agency. It might do you good." So I filled out the application blank: hobbies, measurements, blah, blah, blah. I got a letter: "Congratulations. You have been accepted as an entrant into the Miss Illinois-Universe contest." Now what do I do? I'm stuck.

I won the Miss U.S.A. pageant. I started to laugh. They tell me I'm the only beauty queen in history that didn't cry when she won. It was on network television. I said to myself: "You're kidding." Bob Barker, the host, said: "No, I'm not kidding." I didn't know what else to say at that moment. In the press releases, they call it the great American Dream. There she is, Miss America, your ideal. Well, not my ideal, kid.

The minute you're crowned, you become their property and subject to whatever they tell you. They wake you up at seven o'clock next morning and make you put on a negligee. They serve you breakfast in bed, so that all the New York papers can come in and take your picture sitting in bed, while you're absolutely bleary-eyed from the night before. They put on an expensive negligee, hand you the tray, you take three bites. The photographers leave, you whip off the negligee, they take the breakfast away, and that's it. I never did get any breakfast that day. (*Laughs.*)

You immediately start making personal appearances. The jaycees or the chamber of commerce says: "I want to book Miss U.S.A. for our Christmas Day parade." They pay, whatever it is, seven hundred fifty dollars a day, first-class air fare, round trip expenses, and so forth. If the United Fund calls and wants me to give a five-minute pitch on beauty queens at a luncheon, they still have to pay a fee. It doesn't matter that it's a charity. It's one hundred percent to Miss Universe, Incorporated. You get your salary. That's your prize

"There she is, Miss America, your ideal."

money for the year. I got fifteen thousand dollars, which is all taxed in New York. Maybe out of a check of three thousand dollars, I'd get fifteen hundred dollars.

From the day I won Miss U.S.A. to the day I left for the Miss Universe contest, almost two months, I got a day and a half off. I made about two hundred fifty appearances that year. Maybe three hundred. I snapped ribbons at shopping centers and modelled clothes. The nice thing I got to do was public speaking. They said: "You want a ghost writer?"[3] I said: "No, I know how to talk." I wrote my own speeches. They don't trust the winners to go out and talk, because most of them can't.

At the end of the year, you're run absolutely ragged. That final evening, they usually have several queens from past years come back. Before they crown the new Miss U.S.A., the current one is supposed to take what they call the farewell walk. They call over the PA: Time for the old queen's walk. I'm now twenty-three and I'm an old queen. And they have this idiot farewell speech playing over the airwaves as the old queen takes the walk. You're sitting on the throne for about thirty seconds, then you come down and they

153

announce the name of the new one. You put the crown on her head. And then you're out.

As the new one is crowned, the reporters and photographers rush on the stage. I've seen photographers shove the girl who has just given her reign up thirty seconds before, shove her physically. I was gone by that time. I had jumped off the stage in my evening gown. All of a sudden (*snaps fingers*) you're out. Nobody gives a darn about the old one.

Miss U.S.A. is now in the same graveyard that Emma Knight the twelve-year-old is, where Emma Knight the sixteen-year-old is, and all my past selves. There comes a time when you have to bury those selves because you've grown into another one. You don't keep exhuming[4] the corpses.

If I could sit down with every young girl in America for the next fifty years, I could tell them what I liked about the pageant, and I could tell them what I hated. It wouldn't make any difference. There are always going to be girls who want to enter the beauty pageant. That's the fantasy: the American Dream.

ARNOLD SCHWARTZENEGGER

Call me Arnold.

I was born in a little Austrian town, outside Graz. It was a 300-year-old house.

When I was ten years old, I had the dream of being the best in the world in something. When I was fifteen, I had a dream that I wanted to be the best body builder in the world and the most muscular man. It was not only a dream I dreamed at night. It was also a daydream. It was so much in my mind that I felt it had to become a reality. It took me five years of hard work. Five years later, I turned this dream into reality and became Mr. Universe, the best-built man in the world.

"Winning" is a very important word. There is one person who achieves what he wants to achieve and there are hundreds of thousands who fail. It singles you out: the winner.

When I was a small boy, my dream was not to be big physically, but big in a way that everybody listened to me when I talked. My dream was that I become a very important person, who people recognized and saw as something special. I had a big need for being singled out.

Also my dream was to end up in America. When I was ten years old, I dreamed of being an American. At the time I didn't know much about America, just that it was a wonderful country. I felt it was where I belonged. I didn't like being in a little country like Austria. I did everything possible to get out. I did so in 1968, when I was twenty-one years old.

One of the things I always had was a business mind. When I was in high school, a majority of my classes were business classes. Economics and accounting and mathematics. When I came over here to this country, I really didn't speak English almost at all. I learned English and then started taking business courses, because that's what America is best known for: business; turning one dollar into a million dollars in a short period of time.

Once you have money in your hand, one of the most important things to know is how to keep it. Or how to make more out of it. Real estate is one of the best ways of doing that. I own apartment buildings, office buildings, and raw land. That's my love, real estate.

I have emotions. But what you do, you keep them cold or you store them away for a time. You must control your emotions, you must have command over yourself. Three, four months before a competition, I couldn't interfere in other people's problems. This is sometimes called selfish. But it's the only way you can be if you want to achieve something. Any emotional thing inside me, I try to keep cold so it doesn't interfere with my training.

Many times things really touch me. I feel them and I feel sensitive about them. But I have to talk myself out of it. I have to suppress those feelings in order to go on. Sport is one of those activities where you really have to concentrate. You must pay attention a hundred percent to the particular thing you're doing. There must be nothing else on your mind. Emotions must not interfere. Otherwise, you're thinking about your girlfriend. You're in love, your positive energies get channeled into another direction rather than going into your weight room or making money.

California is to me a dreamland. It is the absolute combination of everything I was always looking for. It has all the money in the world, show business, wonderful weather, beautiful country, and ocean. You can snow ski in the winter, and you can go in the desert

Arnold Schwartzenegger: "I had the dream of being the best."

the same day. You have beautiful-looking people there. They all have a tan.

I believe very strongly in the philosophy of staying hungry. If you have a dream and it becomes a reality, don't stay satisfied with it too long. Make up a new dream and hunt after that one and turn it into reality. When you have achieved that dream, make up a new dream.

I am a strong believer in Western philosophy, the philosophy of success, of progress, of getting rich. The Eastern philosophy is passive. I believe in it maybe three percent of the time. Ninety-seven percent of the time I believe in the Western philosophy of conquering and going on. It's a beautiful philosophy, and Americans should keep it up.

LINDA HAAS, 16

She attends a large technical high school in Chicago. Most of its students are of blue-collar families.

"I live in a changing neighborhood. It's Polish, Spanish, and southern.

"My father is from West Virginia, way up in the mountains. He was a farmer. He was in the Coast Guard. He did a lot of jobs. He was very intelligent, but he refused to go to college. My mother is from a real small town in Missouri. She went to eighth grade, but she was straight A's all the way through. Her stepmother wouldn't let her go to high school. She's bitter over this. My mom really has a thirst for knowledge, and this crushed her."

My father has been a butcher for the A&P for twenty-six years. He never misses a day. He could be dying and he would go to work. The German heritage in him says, you go to work and that's that. I feel sorry for him because he's like a fish out of water. I just feel he would be happier if he could be back in West Virginia.

The company he works for is changed. There was pride. Now it's just falling apart. They're letting people go with no feelings for how long they've worked there. They just lay 'em off. It's sad. He should be getting benefits after all these years and all the sacrifices he's made. Now they're almost ready to lay him off without a word.

They send him from store to store. Before, the only people who did that were the young kids, part-time. My pa is fifty-one. Every week he has to wait to see if they're going to send him to another store. It's humiliating for him after working for them all these years. He's got to call in every so often and find out if they have another store for him. It hurts his feelings. It's just wrong.

He never says it hurts his feelings, he roars. When he's upset, he takes it out by acting angry. He yells about a lot of minor things at home, like the phone bill or if the light doesn't work. He'll roar about it for two hours. I know he couldn't care less about the phone bill or the lights. All the things he'd like to yell at other people about, he's letting out over a light bulb.

I think that for my father and his generation, the dream was to have a home and security and things like that. It was because of the poverty they came from. I don't know what the dream is now. The kids I go to school with, when they talk about their dreams, they don't talk about a home and having money in the bank. It's more like trying to have personal satisfaction. They don't know what they want. I don't know what I want. I don't know what my dreams are. There's so many things I'd like to do, and then . . .

I'd like to be a writer or do some kind of social work. A house in the suburbs just isn't for me. The PTA and the car pool and the house with the mortgage, that doesn't appeal to me. I don't want to be thirty years old with three kids and my Maytag. I would go crazy. My father's worried that I'd marry some very crazy, unorthodox[5] type of eccentric person like me. He'd like to see me marry some nice Joe Citizen that pays all his parking tickets.

I feel old. To me, every day is a day gone, whether you're five, ten, or sixteen. That's sixteen years that are gone now. (*Laughs.*) I don't worry about getting physically old. That doesn't bother me. Just not accomplishing anything and getting old, that bothers me. What have I done in all these sixteen years? Sixteen years is a long time to be alive and not really doing anything but going to school.

LEONEL I. CASTILLO

Former director of the United States Immigration and Naturalization Service (INS).

New immigrants are trying all over again to integrate themselves into the system. They have the same hunger. On any given day, there are about three million throughout the world who are applying to come to the United States and share the American Dream. They are fighting the same battles.

Sometimes the whole family saves up and gives the bright young man or the bright young woman the family savings. It even goes in hock for a year or two. They pin all their hopes on this one kid. They put him on a bus, let him go a thousand miles. He doesn't speak a word of English. He's only seventeen, eighteen years old, but he's gonna save that family. A lot rides on that kid who's a busboy in some hotel.

He's gonna be the first hook, the first pioneer coming into an alien society, the United States. He might be here in Chicago. He works as a busboy all night long. They pay him minimum wage or less, and work him hard. He'll never complain. If he makes a hundred a week, he will manage to send back twenty-five. All over the country, if you go to a Western Union office on the weekend, you'll find a lot of people there sending money orders. In a southwest office, like Dallas, Western Union will tell you seventy-five percent of their business is money orders to Mexico.

After the kid learns a bit, because he's healthy and young and energetic, he'll probably get another job as a busboy. He'll work at another place as soon as the shift is over. He'll try to work his way up to be a waiter. He'll work incredible hours. He doesn't care about union scale, he doesn't care about conditions, about humiliations. He accepts all this as his fate.

He's burning underneath with this energy and ambition. He out-works the U.S. busboys and eventually becomes a waiter. Where he can maneuver, he tries to become the owner and gives a lot of competition to the locals.

It helps me to remember the history of this country. We've always managed, despite our worst actions, to rejuvenate ourselves, to bring in new people. Every new group comes in believing more firmly in the American Dream than the one that came a few years before. Every new group is scared of being in the welfare line or in the unemployment office. They go to night school, they learn about America. We'd be lost without them.

The old dream is still dreamt. The old neighborhood Ma-Pa stores are still around. They are not Italian or Jewish or Eastern European any more. Ma and Pa are now Korean, Vietnamese, Iraqi, Jordanian, Latin American. They live in the store. They work seven days a week. Their kids are doing well in school. They're making it. Sound familiar?

I see all kinds of new immigrants starting out all over again, trying to work their way into the system. They're going through new battles, yet they're old battles. They want to share in the American Dream. The stream never ends.

[1] **intimidated:** frightened; made timid
[2] **resumés:** listings or summaries of a person's experience and background
[3] **ghost writer:** a person who writes a story or speech for someone else
[4] **exhuming:** digging up; bringing back
[5] **unorthodox:** unconventional

A CLOSER LOOK

1. Which of these people are happy with their lives? Which are unhappy?

2. Which interviews do you find most interesting? Why?

3. List elements of "the American Dream" that these people talk about. Define what you think "the American Dream" is.

"Heroes inspire respect; celebrities inspire envy."

Donna Woolfolk Cross

BEING SOMEBODY

● Like Bob Greene (see page 49) and Andy Rooney (see page 53), Donna Woolfolk Cross expresses her unhappiness with some of society's values. Her style of presentation is not as opinionated as theirs are, but she still offers a personal point of view. What makes her ideas convincing are the examples she draws from modern life — examples with which you may be very familiar.

ONE HUNDRED YEARS AGO, PEOPLE BECAME famous for what they had achieved. Men like J. P. Morgan, E. H. Harriman and Jay Gould[1] were all notable achievers. So were Thomas Edison, Mark Twain, and Susan B. Anthony.[2]

Their accomplishments are still evident in our own day. Today's celebrities, however, often do not become known for any enduring achievement. The people we most admire today are usually those who are most highly publicized by the media.

In 1981, a Gallup poll revealed that Nancy Reagan was the nation's "most admired woman." The year before, that distinction went to President Carter's wife, Rosalynn. In fact, the wife of the current President is always one of the nation's most admired women. Today's celebrities, as the writer Daniel Boorstin says, are "people well-known for their well-knownness."

To become such a celebrity, one needs luck, not accomplishment. As Boorstin says, "The hero was distinguished by his achievement; the celebrity by his image or trademark. The hero created himself;

the celebrity is created by the media. The hero was a big man; the celebrity is a big name.''

There is another distinction: heroes inspire respect; celebrities inspire envy. Few of us believe we could be another Jonas Salk[3] or Eleanor Roosevelt,[4] but we could be another TV star like Telly Savalas or Suzanne Somers. Except for the attention they get from the media, these people are exactly like us. We even speak of them with familiarity, as the following headline from a gossip magazine reveals:

BO DEREK GOES APE
OVER HUNKY TARZAN CO-STAR

Such lack of respect would have been unthinkable in a previous era, when people became well-known for more than just their well-knownness.

The shift from hero-worship to celebrity-worship occurred around the turn of the century. It was closely tied to the rise of new forms of media — first photography, and later moving pictures, radio and television. For the first time, Americans could see and recognize their heroes. Previously, men like Gould and Harriman, whose names everyone knew, could easily have passed through a crowd without being recognized. The reproduction of photos in newspapers turned famous people into celebrities whose dress, appearance, and personal habits were widely commented upon. Slowly, the focus of public attention began to shift away from knowing what such people *did* to knowing what they *looked like*.

The shift was accelerated[5] by the arrival of moving pictures. Between 1901 and 1914, 74 percent of the magazine articles about famous people were about political leaders, inventors, professionals, and businessmen. After 1922, however, most articles were about movie stars.

With the arrival of television, the faces of the stars became as familiar as those we saw across the breakfast table. We came to know more about the lives of the celebrities than we did about most of the people we know personally. Less than seventy years after the appearance of the first moving pictures, the shift from hero-worship to celebrity-worship was complete.

Today an appearance on a television talk show is the ultimate proof of ''making it'' in America. Actually, the term ''talk show'' is misleading. Celebrities do not appear on such a program because of an actual desire — or ability — to talk, but simply to gain recognition, and prove, merely by showing up, that they are "somebody."

Being a guest on a talk show does not require qualities of wit, eloquence, brilliance, insight, or intelligence. Craig Tennis, a former talent coordinator for "The Tonight Show," says that when he would ask a scheduled guest, "What would you like to talk to Johnny Carson about?" the reply he got most often was, "Have him ask me anything." This, he says, usually meant, "I am a typical Hollywood actor, so I have never had an original thought and I have nothing to say of any interest to anyone anywhere."

Most hosts are grateful just to get someone who will fill the room with sound. One talk show coordinator comments, "We look for the guest who is sure to talk no matter what. Ten seconds of silence appears very awkward on television; thirty seconds is disastrous. A guest who's got to stop to think about everything he says before he opens his mouth is a ratings nightmare."

This kind of attitude rewards smooth, insincere talk, and makes hesitancy look like stupidity.

"We wouldn't have used George Washington on our show," says one talent coordinator. Mr. Dullsville in person. He might have been first in the hearts of his countrymen, but today he'd be dragging his bottom in the ratings."

[1] **Morgan, Harriman, Gould:** famous bankers and industrialists
[2] **Susan B. Anthony** (1820-1906): reformer who worked for women's rights
[3] **Jonas Salk:** discoverer of the polio vaccine
[4] **Eleanor Roosevelt** (1884-1962): writer, lecturer, and social activist; the wife of President Franklin Delano Roosevelt
[5] **accelerated:** speeded up

A CLOSER LOOK

1. What two concepts is the author contrasting in this essay? Which is associated with the past? Which is associated with the present?

2. Why do you think Cross considers celebrities less valuable than heroes? Do you agree with her? Why or why not?

3. List some people whom you admire. According to Cross' standards, are these people celebrities or heroes?

"When I was seventeen years old, I went to work."

Paddy Chayefsky

PRINTER'S MEASURE

● Does all technological progress benefit humanity? True, machines
may lead to efficiency, but is an increase in efficiency worth the
sacrifice in human happiness? Paddy Chayefsky asks these questions
in this play that was written and produced in the 1950s, during the
"Golden Age" of television drama.

CAST

NARRATOR	MR. FAULKNER
MR. HEALY	LINOTYPIST
BOY (Tom)	WIFE (Mr. Healy's)
SISTER	SON (Mr. Healy's)
MOTHER	DAUGHTER-IN-LAW
NEIGHBOR	(Mr. Healy's)
(Mrs. Gallagher)	UNION OFFICIAL
BOSS	FREIGHT MEN
MR. LUNDY	MECHANIC

ACT I

An old wooden sign sways in a May morning breeze. The words
"Emperor Press" are barely visible. Below, through the dirty
storefront window, are seen a number of samples of the printer's
work. All were printed at least ten years ago and are now dusty with
age.

Narrator: In 1939, when I was seventeen years old, I went to work in a print shop on West 26th Street in New York. . . . *(Lights rise on the inside of the shop — a crowded, dark, damp little place, lit by work bulbs over each press. The floors are black from years of spilled ink and littered with balls of crumpled paper. Along the left wall are three presses: a small job press, a large hand press, and an automatic Kleuge. The Kleuge is clacking away at the moment — its automatic arm plunging with mechanical preciseness.)* My job was to clean the press, fill the fountains with ink . . . a little compositing,[1] and other duties. *(In the shop, the young apprentice sweeps the floor industriously. Seated at an old roll-top desk is a heavyset man in his fifties, wearing a soiled printer's apron. He is frowning at some bills.)* My boss . . . *(A door opens, and a round-shouldered, bowlegged, crusty-looking little man in his sixties comes out, tying his blackened printer's apron behind him.)* The only other worker in the shop was the compositor . . . Mister Healy. I shall never forget Mister Healy as long as I live. *(MR. HEALY opens one of the drawers of the type cabinet, fetches a compositor's stick from the wall behind him, props up his copy, and begins setting up a composition with the sure touch of a finished craftsman. He clamps the frame into place in the press, and then runs off one copy. He holds it up to the light, squinting and frowning, then begins feeding paper into the job press. When he is finished, he pulls one of many wires coming out of the wall, and the press slowly rolls to a halt. He turns to the pile of newly printed copies and begins expertly to straighten them. He darts a quick glance at the BOY.)*

Mr. Healy: Hey! Come here! *(The BOY scurries over. MR. HEALY pulls out a copy and points to a line of print.)* What kind of type is that?

Boy: Twelve-point Clearface.

Mr. Healy: How do you know?

Boy: It's lighter than Goudy, and the lower-case "e" goes up.

Mr. Healy: Clearface is a delicate type. It's clean, it's clear. It's got line and grace. Remember that. Now beat it. *(The BOY hurries back to his cleaning. MR. HEALY regards the unsuspecting figure of the BOSS, bent over his desk, still scowling at his bills.)* Hey!

Boss: What?

Mr. Healy *(waving the copy)*: Why do you keep buying this lightweight stock? It's wrapping paper. How many times I told you not to buy this lightweight stock?

Boss: Watsa matter with you now?

Mr. Healy: If you're going to buy lightweight, buy watermarked, will you? Stop buying this wrapping paper. What are you, a grocery store or a printer? Aren't you ashamed to hand your customers copies like this? *(He lifts his head imperiously.*[2]*)* Hey, boy, come here. *(The BOY, dragging his broom, scurries down the length of the shop. MR. HEALY thrusts the paper at him again.)* Feel that. It offends your fingers, don't it? It has no texture, no taste. When I get some, I'll show you how to feel paper. Wrap these up neat. It goes out this afternoon. *(He turns abruptly and shuffles down to the front of the shop, muttering to himself.)* Lightweight paper . . . it demeans[3] the craft. *(He raises his voice for the benefit of the BOSS.)* This place is turning into a real Sixth Avenue shop, a real dump. *(He plucks a printed sheet from the Kleuge press and examines it with a scowl. He takes a measuring stick from a pocket, lays it on the printed page, and measures the margin. With a quick, scornful glance at the BOSS, he bends over and resets the press the tiniest fraction of an inch. The BOY stands behind him, watching, open-eyed with fascination. MR. HEALY winks suddenly at the BOY, then abruptly goes back to resetting the press.)* Boy, if you was my kid, I wouldn't even let you near a print shop. It'll take you twenty years before you're even a half-good printer. By the time you're a printer, you could be ten doctors. I got a boy, thirty-eight years old. When he was fifteen, he said to me, he wanted to quit school and work down in the shop with me. I whacked him one across the head; he's still talking about it. *(The BOY waits, then, deciding the speech is over, he starts back to his chores.)* Stay here, boy! When I say printer, I mean printer. I don't mean these kids, come out of some school, come walking in, tell you they're compositors. *(He indicates the copy propped up in front of him.)* Whoever set this up is a real Sixth Avenue printer. Look at this "W." The face is breaking in half — I don't like Bodoni. It looks like a vaudeville poster. There's no design here. There's no flow in the lines. There's no grace. The compositor who set this up, he figures it's just a lousy consignment[4] book. He just threw a handful of type together, and flopped it in the press. *(He waves a finger at the BOY.)* A good compositor takes a poor consignment book like this and sets it up like he was Michelangelo painting the Sistine Chapel. *(The* BOY *starts to go.)* Hey, boy! *(The* BOY *turns.)*

Boy: Yes, Mister Healy.

Mr. Healy: Do you like this trade?

Boy: Yes, Mister Healy, I like it very much.

Mr. Healy: You'll never get that ink out from under your nails. You're going to have dirty fingernails the rest of your life.

Boy: I like printing very much, Mister Healy.

(The old man suddenly reaches out and awkwardly pats the BOY *on the side of the head. Then he looks down at the paper in his other hand. He mutters.)*

Mr. Healy: If you was my kid, boy, I wouldn't even let you near a print shop.

(The BOY, *quite touched, goes back to his work. Lights fade, rise on the* NARRATOR.*)*

Narrator: I remember one morning Mister Healy came in, clutching a brown package.

(Lights rise on MR. HEALY, *entering the shop with a thin parcel about the size of a book.)*

Mr. Healy: Hey, boy, come here. *(The* BOY *obligingly sidles down to the old man, who unwraps the package, carefully extracts a thin, brown book, and slowly extends it to the* BOY. *The* BOY *reaches for it.)* Don't touch it, boy. Just look at it. *(The old man slowly opens a beautiful leather-bound book. The paper is thick and soft, the printing exquisite. The* BOY *is impressed.)*

Boy: It's beautiful, Mister Healy.

(The old man's face glows with an almost forgotten sense of craftsmanship.)

Mr. Healy *(in a whisper)*: I set that book myself, every bit of it. In 1922 I printed it and bound it, and I bought the leather for the cover. You don't see books like that around. I etched that cover. I etched it myself. With a red-hot needle. With my hands, I did it, boy, with my hands. There wasn't a machine in the whole process. Isn't it clear? Look how level the impressions are. Look how the letters seem to cling to the paper. Oh, it's a beauty! A rare piece of work! A rare piece!

Boy: It's beautiful, Mister Healy.

Mr. Healy: Do you really mean it?

Boy: I really mean it, Mister Healy.

(MR. HEALY begins to rewrap the book.)

Mr. Healy *(without looking up)*: I'll buy you a soda tonight before you go home.

(Lights fade, rise again on the shop. It is morning. The old wall clock reads nine o'clock. The BOY enters in street clothes.)

Narrator: This is the story of Mister Healy and the linotype machine. . . .

Boy: Good morning, Mister Healy.

(The old man says nothing, just deepens his scowl.)

Mr. Healy *(waving his composing stick and roaring)*: I quit! That's all! I'll finish this off, and then I quit! *(The BOSS casts a glance of appeal to the ceiling and goes back to his press.)* I won't work in no shop that's got a linotype machine!

Boss: Ah, come on, John, act your age.

(The two old friends bellow at each other, without pausing in their work.)

Mr. Healy: You heard me!

Boss: Act your age.

Mr. Healy: Better call the union, get another printer.

Boss: If you had your way, printers would still be carving letters out of wood.

Mr. Healy: I ain't working in no shop that's got a linotype machine. I'm a printer; I ain't a stenographer. A linotype machine ain't

"I don't want no linotype machine in this shop."

nothing but a big typewriter. I ain't working here no more.

Boss: Yeah, sure.

Mr. Healy: Better send the boy to the bank, pick up my close-out pay.

Boss: You'll be working here when we're all dead.

Mr. Healy: Yeah?

Boss: Why should I send out eight thousand bucks worth of linotype to Schmidt every year? I can set that stuff up right here.

Mr. Healy: I don't want no linotype machine in this shop.

Boss: John, we been friends for twenty-seven years, so I'm taking the privilege of telling you you're an old lunatic. Every time I bring a new machine into this shop, you raise the roof. When I brought in the automatic Kleuge, you threw a can of ink right through the window. All right, I'm telling you, I need a linotype machine in this shop. You can't set everything up by hand. Those days is gone forever.

Mr. Healy: Yeah?

Boss: Yeah. You're still living in the Middle Ages. We do printing with machines now. I'm going to haul this old job press out. Tomorrow morning, there's going to be a linotype machine which cost me twenty-eight hundred dollars sitting right over there where that old job press is now. You just get used to the idea.

(Lights fade, rise on the interior of a dairy cafeteria. MR. HEALY *and the* BOY, *carrying trays of food, make their way to a table. They sit beside another old-timer cut from the same mold as* MR. HEALY. *His name is* LUNDY.)

Mr. Healy: They're putting in a linotype machine in my shop.

Mr. Lundy *(sympathetic)*: Is that right, John? Well, that's a bad bit of news, isn't it?

Mr. Healy: Oh, it is. I don't know what the trade is coming to. There's nothing but machines. He's got so many machines now in that shop, I don't know whether it's a print shop, or he's manufacturing Chevrolets. He says to me this morning — and the boy here will bear witness — the day of the handcraftsman is gone forever.

Mr. Lundy: That's not what I had in mind, John. I was thinking that you might be out of a job soon.

Mr. Healy: Oh, don't be daft. I've been in that shop for twenty-seven years. It would crumble to dust without me.

Mr. Lundy: Oh, I've heard those gallant words before. Didn't I say them myself? For isn't it just what happened to me? The boss installed a row of linotypes, and within the week I was out on the street, poking my head into shops, looking for a job. I haven't had an apron on for seven weeks, John.

Mr. Healy *(frowning)*: I'm not worried about my job. Why, the boss don't blow his nose, he doesn't let me measure it off with a pica^5 stick for him first. Ask the boy here. I can walk into any shop in New York and command a hundred dollars a week, and they'd wrench their bones loose jumping for me. *(*MR. LUNDY *nods sadly.)* Seven weeks is it now, Lundy, that you haven't worked?

Mr. Lundy: Seven weeks, and I expect a lot more. Work is rare. It's not like the old days when you could just march into a shop, pick up an apron, and go to work.

(Lights fade, rise on the interior of a bar where MR. HEALY *and an old friend named* FAULKNER *sit in coats and hats.)*

Mr. Faulkner: . . . Well, I give you six weeks before he cans you.

Mr. Healy: Well, you're Mister Cheerful today, aren't you, George?

Mr. Faulkner: Give the facts a good look in the face, John. When your boss brings in a linotype machine, what's he need a compositor for? For a couple of hundred bucks, he buys himself a supply of type, and he'll be rattling off printed matter like shelling peas.

Mr. Healy: The boss is an old friend. He's been up to my house a hundred times. He's an old friend, and he isn't going to can me just like that.

Mr. Faulkner: Aye, and wasn't my last boss an old friend who had been to the house for dinner more often than he ate at his own home. Well, four months ago he calls me into the office, and he says: "George, I'm thinking of expanding a bit — magazines, and pamphlets, and that sort of thing. I'm bringing in a pair of linotype machines, and I just want you to know you've nothing to worry about." Well, two weeks had barely sneaked by when he called me into the office, and he says: "George, we're closing out the hand-press department. You're fired." Well, he's no friend of mine no more. . . . Oh, things are bad. There isn't work around for no one. My old boss, fourteen years ago, Old Man Kleinberg, flung himself off the roof of the Stowe Building yesterday. There was a bit in the papers about it, did you see it, John? I'm sorry to hear about that linotype, John. But if you like, we can go job-hunting together.

Mr. Healy: Well, I'm surely glad I bumped into you, George. You've brightened my day immeasurably.

Mr. Faulkner: It's my disposition to be cheerful. . . . Oh, it's a bad year for printers. . . . Well, cheers.

(Lights fade, rise on the Healy home, where MR. HEALY, *his wife, his* SON *(38), his* DAUGHTER-IN-LAW *(35), and his* GRANDDAUGHTER *(14) are eating dinner. They eat in silence — oppressed by the old man's gloom.)*

Mr. Healy: . . . So I thought I'd try it out, see if things was as bad as all that. So I went up to Sixth Avenue and opened the door and leaned into the shop, and I said, "Need a good comp?" And the boss there just looked up and shook his head. And then I tried another shop. "Need a good comp?" And it was the same. And I must have poked my head into half a dozen shops, and, oh, it was like 1931, when the whole town was gray and locked up, and you had that dreadful feeling that there wasn't a dollar in the whole city, and the men lined up for blocks to buy a bowl of rice for a penny.

Son: Oh, now, Dad, it isn't as bad as that.

Wife: Well, it's a shame now, isn't it? A shame and a scandal that a man devotes his whole life to a trade, to be cast off at the age of sixty-six for a machine.

Son: Now, he hasn't been canned yet, Ma. We're all being a bit premature. The boss is an old friend. He's been up to this house a hundred times. . . . And if he cans you, then what? You're sixty-six years old, Dad, with a good bit in the bank. You've worked a full life, and perhaps it's time, Dad, to enjoy the autumn of your years.

Mr. Healy *(raising his head imperiously)*: The autumn of my years?

Son: You'll sleep till ten, and no more elbowing about in the subways.

Daughter-in-law: I sometimes wish I was sixty-six so I could sit in the park and contrive ways to spend my pension.

Mr Healy: Oh, do you?

Son: Perhaps you'll buy a little car and go bucketing down to Florida with Ma, and play checkers with the old chaps down there. Take it easy and loll in the sun — the rewards of a fruitful life.

Daughter-in-law *(to granddaughter)*: Eat your soup. The rest of us are on the meat already.

Son: You'll be out of that musty shop, Dad. What a place to work!

Mr. Healy *(stands and stares at his* SON, *aghast)*: That's my trade, man! That's my trade! I'd crumble into my coffin without my trade! *(He takes a step from the table, stops.)* I love that work! I'd rather be a printer than ambassador to Ireland! *(He stares at them, then turns and goes into his room. The others pause, then begin eating again.)*

Son: Well, he hasn't been canned yet, and there's no sense being premature. We'll just have to wait and see what happens. . . .

(Lights dim, rise on the print shop. Two sweating FREIGHT MEN, *the* BOSS, *and the* BOY *are trying to dolly a huge linotype machine down a ramp into the shop. This spectacular operation has attracted quite a group of sidewalk spectators, who are lined*

up outside the front window, pressing their noses against the glass. AD LIBS: "Watch your fingers, you nut!" . . . "Watch out, the wheels is coming off on this side." . . . "Get your end over, will you?" . . . "Hey, get those kids outta there." The machine is wheeled into the empty area left by the removed job press. AD LIBS: "How far in you want it, boss?" . . . "That's fine right where it is." . . . "Boy, I'm sweating like a dog. This must weigh twenty-five tons." Slowly the heavy machine is levered into place. A magnificent engineering feat has just been accomplished, and the FREIGHT MEN, *the* BOSS, *the* BOY, *and the spectators are all impressed and hushed. The* BOSS, *his chest heaving from his exertion, looks down on the linotype machine with understandable pride.* MR. HEALY *stands in the shadows in the rear of the shop, regarding the linotype machine with patent hatred and gloom. He leans to the* BOY.)

Mr. Healy: That machine'll be the death of me, boy. *(He turns abruptly and heads off for the washroom. Lights fade.)*

ACT II

Narrator: And so the linotype machine was brought into the shop, and a linotypist was hired — and Mr. Healy declared war on both of them. First he challenged the machine to a race. *(In the shop the* BOY *raises his hand like the timer at a foot race. The* LINOTYPIST *sits poised at his machine, ready to start.* MR. HEALY, *composing stick in hand, waits for the signal. The* LINOTYPIST *nods. The* BOY's *arm comes down, and the race is on. The* LINOTYPIST's *fingers flick rapidly over the keys. Then, with a broad smile, he lifts his head. He's done.* MR. HEALY, *muttering, examines his own half-finished line of type.)* Then he took the tack that the linotype machine had a personal grudge against him. *(*MR. HEALY *enters the small area separating the Kleuge press from the linotype machine. He bends down to pick up a sheet of paper. When he straightens up, he bangs his head against a projecting edge of the linotype machine. He eyes the machine, daring it to try that again. Muttering, he starts for the back of the shop, pauses, looks around to see if anyone is watching him, then gives the machine a quick kick.* MR. HEALY *begins coughing.)* Or else he would suddenly be seized with a paroxysm of coughing, which he claimed was due to lead fumes that were filling the shop. He would look around at the rest of us, amazed that we were immune to it all.

(Lights fade, rise on the living room of the BOY's drab, lower-class apartment. The boy's MOTHER sits stiffly in an old chair, her hands folded limply in her lap. Her face is drawn. In the next chair sits a NEIGHBOR, mumbling words of concern to the MOTHER. The BOY and his SISTER, a girl of about 20, are standing by the darkened window. All three of the family wear black mourning bands.)

Narrator: In June 1939, my father died.

Neighbor: Oh, he was a man of cheer. Wherever he went, he brought a spark of laughter. I've been weeping myself dry these last four days. *(The doorbell rings.)*

Mother: Tom, go see the door.

(The BOY starts down the hallway to the door.)

Neighbor: It seems that all the good folks are dropping off these days. Now, if there are so many heart attacks, why couldn't one be visited upon our landlord, who didn't give us a pound of steam this whole last winter and hasn't painted our flat since we moved in?

(The BOY opens the door. Standing in the doorway is MR. HEALY.)

Mr. Healy: Hello, boy . . .

Boy *(shocked by this visit)*: Hello, Mister Healy.

Mr. Healy: I hope you don't mind, but I brought a basket of fruits which I think is customary on these occasions. *(He gives the BOY a small basket of fruit.)*

Boy: That's very nice of you, Mister Healy. Really, that's very nice of you. *(He is obviously touched.)* I mean, that's nice of you to come over and pay your respects. Would you like to come in the house, meet my mother and sister? *(He leads the old man to the room.)* Ma, this is Mister Healy, who is the compositor down at the shop. He's brought a basket of fruit.

(MR. HEALY offers his hand to the MOTHER.*)*

Mother: Thank you very much, Mister Healy.

Boy: That's my sister.

Sister: How do you do, Mister Healy. *(The old man nods.)*

Neighbor: He was a man of cheer, Mister Healy.

Mr. Healy: I'm sure he was.

Neighbor: Wherever he went, he brought a spark of laughter. He was struck down in the prime, and what will his family do? He left behind him only a pittance of insurance, which has gone into the rental of the hearse and a plot of grave.

Mother: Missus Gallagher . . .

Neighbor: And the girl two years away from graduation.

Mother: Missus Gallagher, Mister Healy has come to pay his respects, not to take away the furniture.

Neighbor: He was a man of cheer.

Mr. Healy: I'm sure he was. *(A short, uncomfortable silence falls over the group.)* Well, I'll say good-bye then. I just came by to let you know you have a friend whom you might not have known about.

Mother: Thank you, Mister Healy.

(The old man turns abruptly and starts back down the hallway. The BOY *follows him. When they reach the door, the old man pauses.)*

Mr. Healy *(in a low voice)*: Do you need some money, boy?

Boy *(also in a low voice)*: I don't think so, Mister Healy.

Mr. Healy: When will you be back at the shop?

Boy: In a couple of days, I guess.

Mr. Healy: Are you sad?

Boy: I haven't had time to be sad, Mister Healy. Ten minutes after my old man collapsed on the floor, my Uncle Frank had me in the kitchen telling me I had to start making a better living. Because my mother doesn't know a trade, you know. She can't even type. And my sister is two years in college, and my mother won't hear of her quitting, and somebody's got to pay the rent. We can't stay here. It's four hundred dollars a month here, gloomy as it is. I was thinking of asking the boss for a raise. Do you think he'll give it to me?

"Really, that's very nice of you."

Mr. Healy: Sure he will. You're the best boy we ever had in the shop.

Boy: I was thinking of asking four dollars an hour. That's only one hundred and sixty dollars a week. . . . *(The strain of the week is beginning to tell on the* BOY. *He begins to cry quietly even as he talks.)* He was a tough guy, my old man. He gave me a lot of hard times, but we used to get along good. . . .

Mr. Healy: Oh, it's a lot of responsibility you have for a seventeen-year-old. But you'll make out. I'll talk to the boss first thing in the morning, and when you'll come back, you'll be four dollars an hour. And I'll teach you to composite. You've got the feel for it, boy. You'll make a good printer some day. *(The gentle words of sympathy only unleash a new flood of tears. The old man smiles fondly at the* BOY, *then puts an arm around his shoulder. The* BOY *rests his head on the old man's chest and cries.* MR. HEALY's *own eyes are a little wet.)* We'll make a good printer out of you, boy.

(Lights fade, rise on the boy's MOTHER *at home, lying on the sofa in an old robe. It is some hours later, and she is ready for*

bed. She stares at the ceiling. TOM *comes in.)*

Mother: Tom, go to bed.

Boy: Are you going to sleep out here again tonight, Ma?

Mother: Yes.

Boy: Listen, Ma, I've been thinking. I know how determined you are that Polly finishes college, but I think it's pretty silly. *(The* MOTHER *makes a soft "shush," and indicates a closed door with a nod of her head.)* Look, the best I can make right now is one hundred and sixty dollars a week, and —

Mother: You better come over here, Tom. *(The* BOY *rises a little sulkily, pads across the room to his* MOTHER, *and stands over her.)*

Boy: Ma, after six months I might get a small raise, maybe another couple of bucks a week, and I mean, now, let's be sensible.

Mother: Tom . . . .

Boy: So what if she goes to college? I don't see what's so important.

Mother: All right, don't talk so loud.

Boy *(whispering)*: I think she ought to go out and get a job, contribute to the house. She can get some kind of a job, and if she can make another one hundred and sixty dollars a week, then we'd be all right. But this way she don't earn nothing, and she has to buy all those books every term. She must spend a hundred bucks every term just on books. We can't afford that, Ma. You know that.

Mother: We can manage.

Boy: We can't manage.

Mother: It gives me pleasure that she goes to college. She has a fine mind, and it would be criminal to take her from her classes.

Boy: What does a girl have to go to college for? She's just going to get married. She'll have babies, and in ten years she won't remember one chemical from another. Physics! I mean, what is she studying physics for? What is she going to do with her physics?

Mother: All right, Tom, sit down.

Boy: She's a good-looking girl. Why don't she get married? Who does she think she is?

Mother: Tom, I know you feel bitter against your sister.

Boy: I don't feel bitter.

Mother: You do. I can see every thought in your mind. You're

178

going to have to scrape and scrimp to put a sister through college. And you're only seventeen years old. You'd like to be out kissing girls instead of worrying under the burden of a grown man. Well, it'll only be two years. She'll crowd in as much as is humanly possible and finish it off quick. She's very good at this physics, and someday she may poke out some radium like Madame Curie, and they'll make a moving picture out of her. You're as old-fashioned as your father, and all that you see in a woman is a drudge to cook your stew. Well, times have changed, and it's something marvelous that a sister of yours has a turn of mind to explore atoms. I can't tell you the pleasure it gives me to see her bent over her books; and when she's not home, sometimes I open up her notes and see these fantastic diagrams and pictures, and I never get over the shock of it. If she was just another student, I'd have said to her long since, you've got to go to work. But she's strong at this physics, Tom. She'll make something out of it. I'm not going to argue from day to night about this with you, Tom, as I did with your father. It's got to be clear between us.

Boy: All right, all right.

Mother: Not all right, all right. When I was a girl, your father came to my father's house and knocked at the door and announced: "I'm after a bride." And he and my father went into the other room and talked it out, and I sat in the kitchen with my hands in my lap and waited to hear. I thought nothing of it, because it was done that way when I was a girl. But the world is changing, and, if a woman's got a spark, it's her right and privilege to make a thing of herself. It's like this old friend of yours in the shop. The machine is there, but he won't accept it. I'm not saying that it's good or bad that a machine does a man out of his work, but the machine is here. It's part of our world, and the thing to do is to make our lives better with the machine, not worse. If we cannot hold on to old things, we must make peace with the new. Your sister has a talent. You had best make peace with that, Tom.

Boy: It's the truth, Ma. She's a clever girl, and you know that I'm very proud of her underneath. You know what I mean, Ma?

Mother: I know what you mean, Tom. You're a solid boy, and I think very wise for your years. Else I couldn't talk to you as I do.

Boy: It was only natural that I should feel a little bitter.

Mother: It was only natural, Tom.

Boy: But it's going to be hard, Ma. One hundred and sixty bucks a week. Maybe, I could pick up a side job somewhere. It's going to be hard.

Mother: Oh, don't I know that.

Boy *(smiling):* You're a decent woman, Ma, and just to show you how much I like you, I'll go get you a blanket out of your bedroom.

Mother: No, Tom, the talk has done me a lot of good. I don't think I'll mind sleeping in the old room again.

Boy: I'm going to bed. *(He starts off, shaking his head and muttering.)* It's going to be hard. . . .

(He exits through the door. The MOTHER, *still lying on the sofa, suddenly closes her eyes and a trace of a smile appears on her thin face. Lights fade, rise on the* LINOTYPIST *working at his machine in the shop. Beside him is a small stove for melting down lead. Along the wall are about a dozen "pigs" — small oblong chunks of lead. The* BOY *is watching the* LINOTYPIST *with quiet fascination.)*

Linotypist: Put another pig in.

(The BOY *nods, takes a pig from the wall, and drops it carefully into the pot.)*

Boy: How much you make a week, Joe?

Linotypist: Two hundred and fifty.

Boy: No kidding.

Linotypist: Yeah.

Boy: That's a lot of money. Mister Healy only makes two hundred, and he's sixty-six years old.

Linotypist: I made as high as four hundred. I once worked for a couple of guys on Broadway and 25th. They had four linotypes and a proof press. You know, little shops like this one here, they don't usually have a linotype machine. They usually send their linotype work out. Thirty cents a line — *(His hands flick over the keys, and a line of lino flips out onto the plate.)* Thirty cents!

Boy: It must be tough to get to be a linotyper.

Linotypist: Aaah, you go to school for a year. That's all I went. Then I went to Paterson, New Jersey, for a joint called The

Monarch Publications, Inc. Used to print comic books. That wasn't bad. At least, it was interesting work. Then I got a job in Buffalo, New York. Used to print fire-insurance laws. That's all I ever printed there, fire-insurance laws. Used to drive me crazy. Sorry I ever left those comic books. Of course, that was nonunion work, only paid ninety bucks. But I always remembered those comic books. That was the only interesting material I ever worked on. You ever read a comic book called *Jungle Judy*?

Boy: No.

Linotypist: Boy, that was good. Hey, kid, put in another pig. *(The* BOY *puts in another pig.)*

Boy: All you went was one year in linotyping school?

Linotypist: Yeah.

(The BOY *ponders this for a moment. Then he looks down the shop to where* MR. HEALY *is bent over the stone.)*

Mr. Healy: Hey, boy, you've got four trays of distribution waiting for you.

Boy: Okay, Mister Healy. What's the name of that school, Joe?

Linotypist: American Linotyping School.

Mr. Healy: Hey, boy, did you hear me?

Boy: Yeah, okay, Mister Healy.

Linotypist: Before you go, kid, put in another pig.

Boy: It's pretty full now, Joe. It may spurt.

Linotypist: It won't. Put it in.

(The BOY *picks up a pig.* MR. HEALY *regards the* LINOTYPIST *and his machine with a look of great scorn.)*

Mr. Healy: Oh, this is a very clever machine you have here. Oh, look at the little things flipping around like bugs. But it broke down yesterday, didn't it? It took three hours and eighty dollars for a mechanic before you was able to clack away again.

Linotypist: What do you want from me now? Why are you always bothering me? Do I always bother you?

Mr. Healy: Well, now —

Linotypist: Do I always come down the front and stick my head over your shoulder, while you're piddling away with that crummy hand type?

"Crummy hand type, is it?"

Mr. Healy: Crummy hand type, is it?

Linotypist: Leave me alone for a couple of minutes, will you? *(to the* BOY*)* This old looney, he drives me crazy.

Boss *(calling from the back of the shop)*: Hey, John, leave the man alone, will you?

Mr. Healy: I was just commenting on the fact that it took three hours and —

Boss: All right, John —

Mr. Healy: — eighty dollars to set this machine —

Linotypist: He's driving me nuts, this old character.

Mr. Healy: — back into operating condition yesterday.

Linotypist: These old comps, they're all off their rockers. I come in here yesterday, I find him standing in the middle of the shop, cussing out the machine like it was human. *(to the* BOY*)* Put that pig in, will you?

(The BOY *drops the pig in.)*

Boy: Watch it, it's spurting!

Mr. Healy *(roaring to the world at large)*: Did you see that! Did you see that! Did you see that!

Boss: What happened, John?

Linotypist: Aaah, it just spurted. It just stings a minute.

Mr. Healy *(holding out his hands like a trophy)*: The unholy thing sprayed me! Did you see that now!

Linotypist: I been sprayed a hundred times.

Mr. Healy: Suppose it had gone into my eye? We'll all be blind before the year is out! The machine's a hazard to one and all.

Boss: All right, John, what are you yelling about?

Mr. Healy *(still holding his hand out)*: This unholy monster is a threat to life and limb, and I demand that it leave this shop! Either it goes, or I go! But I'll not take my life in my hands from this moment!

Linotypist: You just got a couple of lead drops on your arm. Just wipe them off.

Mr. Healy: Did you hear me, boss?

Boss: All right, all right, take it easy, will you? Nothing happened. The pot spurted a little. *(MR. HEALY thrusts his arm out for the BOSS to see.)*

Mr. Healy: Will you look at it? Mottled with lead!

Boss *(roaring)*: All right, John! Cut it out, will you! You'd think it was radioactive, for goodness sake! It's just lead! Wipe it off! And stay away from the linotyper, will you! You're really driving me crazy!

(The old man stares up at the BOSS, *shocked by his old friend's anger. Then he abruptly turns and starts back down to the front of the shop. Lights fade, rise on the exterior of a building with engraved lettering on the door: "United Brotherhood of Printers, Linotypers, and Pressmen." Inside,* MR. HEALY *sits stiffly in front of a desk. Behind the desk sits a slim, dark, sympathetic young man wearing glasses.)*

Mr. Healy: My name is Healy. I been a member of this union since it was founded. I've never been remiss in my dues, and I want to register a complaint. I'm a compositor. I work in a small shop, the Emperor Press, at 283 West 26th Street, a bit of a shop, two job presses and a small Kleuge. I've worked there for twenty-seven years. Eight weeks ago, my boss installed a linotype machine, which is a safety hazard and a danger to the whole community. *(The* UNION OFFICIAL *smiles patiently.)* The shop is always filled with poisonous lead fumes which is leading me to an early grave, and just this afternoon the horrible machine burst into a geyser of molten lead, covering me from head to foot. You better make some notes on this, boy. Now, I'm sure this machine is a violation of some safety rule or another, and I want to have it removed. (MR. HEALY *now contrives a few coughs.*) It may very well be I have taken a case of tuberculosis as a result of those poisonous lead fumes.

Union Official: Does the boss have a hose running through the wall to the street?

Mr. Healy *(scowling)*: Yes.

Union Official: Does he have a permit from the Department of Labor for that machine?

Mr. Healy *(looking down at his gnarled hands; in a low voice)*: Yes.

(*The* UNION OFFICIAL *leans forward sympathetically.*)

Union Official: Mr. Healy, the truth of it is that you just don't like the machine. Isn't that the truth of it? (MR. HEALY *makes no answer.*) My old man was like you, Mr. Healy. He hated machines. Printing was a hand trade to him. It didn't make any difference if he was setting up a bill book or a Bible. When he died, he wanted to be buried in his apron. (*He smiles sympathetically.*) If you want us to, Mr. Healy, we'll send a man down to look it over.

(*MR. HEALY rises slowly.*)

Mr. Healy *(muttering)*: No need. (*He turns and shuffles toward the door.*) When I die, I'll be buried in my apron, too, if I'm not asphyxiated by these poisonous lead fumes first.

(*He opens the door and exits. Lights fade, rise on the shop. MR. HEALY comes in, dressed as usual in hat and worn topcoat. Muttering to himself, he moves past the BOY, who is standing by the type cabinets. He takes off his coat, jacket, and tie, and hangs them up. He picks up his apron and begins to tie it on. The BOSS comes over to him.*)

Boss: I'm sorry, John, I lost my temper, but you know you can drive somebody crazy. *(The old man doesn't even look at him.)* Come on, John, what do you say? I'll buy you a drink after work tonight —

(MR. HEALY moves past the LINOTYPIST and joins the BOY at the type cabinets. He fetches his composing stick off the nail, opens a drawer, and begins to set type. The BOY and MR. HEALY now stand shoulder to shoulder, each before an open drawer of type. MR. HEALY is muttering.)

Boy: Did you say something, Mister Healy?

Mr. Healy *(muttering a little louder)*: I said, I want you to stay an hour after work tonight. I'm going to give you your first lesson in compositing. I'm going to make a printer out of you. This is a great trade. It's not going to be crushed under a bunch of machines.

(The BOY is obviously disturbed. He continues working for a moment.)

Boy: I can't make it tonight, Mister Healy.

Mr. Healy: What's the matter?

Boy: I got an appointment. I'm filling out an application for a school.

Mr. Healy: What school?

Boy: A linotyping school.

Mr. Healy: What are you talking about?

Boy: Mister Healy, I got a mother and a sister to support. My sister won't be out of college for two years. I spoke to the boss about it. He says he'll let me off an hour early every night, and I can go to this linotyping school in the evenings. *(The BOY hasn't looked up once during this explanation. MR. HEALY stares at him.)*

Mr. Healy: Hey, boy —

(The BOY turns to look at MR. HEALY. Suddenly the old man's hand lashes out and strikes the BOY flat across the face. The BOY regards the trembling old man for a moment, then turns back to work. MR. HEALY slowly turns back to his own work. They work in silence. The lights fade.)

185

ACT III

Mr. Healy's WIFE, SON, *and* GRANDDAUGHTER *are sitting in their home at night, listening to the radio.* MR. HEALY *is nowhere to be seen. The doorbell buzzes. The* SON *opens the door. The* BOY *is standing there.*

Son: Yes, sir?

Boy: I'd like to see Mr. Healy, if he's in. I'm the boy that works down his shop.

Son: What's that?

Boy: I said I'm the boy who works down his shop.

Son: Oh. Oh, well, come on in. Just a minute. *(He starts for the bedroom door.)*

Wife: Is anything wrong, George?

Son: It's a kid from the old man's shop.

(The SON *knocks gently on* MR. HEALY's *door and opens it a bit. It is a small, two-by-four bedroom containing little more than a bed, a dresser, a lamp, and a straight-back chair. There is no light in the room, just what streams in through the door and a trace of moonlight that outlines the furniture.* MR. HEALY *is sitting stiffly in his chair, his hands folded in his lap. He is deep in reverie. He looks up — a little startled.)*

Mr. Healy: What is it, George?

Son: There's a boy from your shop to see you.

Mr. Healy: Who?

Son: A boy from your shop.

Mr. Healy: From my shop? Oh. Well, send him in.

(The SON *turns and beckons to the* BOY, *who enters the room.* MR. HEALY *turns to him.)*

Mr. Healy: Hello, boy, is something wrong?

Boy: No, I just came by because of the fight we had, and I felt so lousy about it, you know what I mean? So I asked the boss for your address, and I just came up, that's all, to apologize if I said anything to hurt you.

Mr. Healy *(to his* SON*):* Close the door, George. *(The* SON *closes*

186

the door behind him, leaving MR. HEALY *and the* BOY *in the darkness.)* Well, sit down, boy.

(The BOY *sits on the bed.)*

Boy: I'm sorry if I said anything to get you mad, Mister Healy.

Mr. Healy: Well, I surely had no call to smack you one like that. I'm not your father.

Boy: I know how you feel about linotyping and things like that.

Mr. Healy: Well, that's how I feel. I surely can't expect all the world to shake my hand.

Boy: I don't run across many people who I really like, Mister Healy, and I sure don't want to have any bad feelings between us.

Mr. Healy: Thank you, boy. *(a pause)* Did you go to that school?

Boy: Yes.

Mr. Healy: Did you get accepted?

Boy: Well, I filled out the papers. It costs quite a chunk of money. I'll have to talk further with my Ma, and probably my Uncle Charlie, who will have to loan me the tuition. But the school guarantees to get you a job as soon as you graduate. Out in the sticks somewhere, but I think it's worth the investment.

Mr. Healy: Well, you've got a lot of responsibilities, and you've got to think of those.

Boy: Yes . . . Mister Healy, look at it this way. If I just stick around, I guess I could learn the trade, and, maybe when I'm about forty, I could say I was a compositor and get a pretty good wage. And then what? If I work steady and save some dough, maybe when I'm fifty I could get a mortgage on some little shop somewhere. Out in the sticks somewhere, printing up wedding invitations, ten bucks for a hundred. Maybe I can make three, four hundred a week. I take in some stationery supplies and sell Christmas cards, and where do I go from there? This way, bang! One year out of school, I'll make two hundred and fifty bucks out in New Jersey. I know that sounds like all I'm interested in is money, but you got to take a realistic view of these things.

Mr. Healy: Sure, boy.

Boy: I like printing. I get a real kick out of it. I mean sometimes, when I'm feeding the press, I forget that it's nothing but an old, broken-down machine. I think to myself, that's a monster who's going to snap off my fingers if I don't keep him tame.

Mr. Healy: I often have the same image myself.

Boy: When I go out on deliveries, I always wear my apron because I want everybody in the street to know I'm a printer.

Mr. Healy: Boy, I never met a linotyper who liked his job.

Boy: They like their job on payday, I bet you.

Mr. Healy: They sit all day, plunking keys. There's no craft to it. There's no pride.

Boy: Nowadays, I don't know you have to be so proud. Mister Healy, I just figure there ain't much future in being a compositor. I mean, what's wrong with linotyping? If they print all the books in thousands and thousands of copies?

Mr. Healy: Are there so many good books around? Are the authors any more clever?

Boy: How are you going to set up daily newspapers? You can't supply the public demand for printed matter by hand setting.

Mr. Healy: Are the people any wiser than they were a hundred years ago? Are they happier? This is the great American disease, boy! This passion for machines. Everybody is always inventing labor-saving devices. What's wrong with labor? A man's work is the sweetest thing he owns. It would do us a lot better to invent some labor-making devices. We've gone mad, boy, with this mad chase for comfort, and it's sure we're losing the very juice of living. It's a sad business! They sit a row of printers down in a line, and the machine clacks, and the mats flip, and when it comes out, the printer has about as much joy of creation as the delivery boy. There's no joy in this kind of life, boy — no joy. It's a very hard two, three hundred dollars a week, I'll tell you that!

Boy (*staring down at his feet*): Well, I don't agree with you, Mister Healy.

Mr. Healy: Aye, it's very hard to want to be poor when you're seventeen.

Boy: The world changes, Mister Healy. The old things go by, and each of us must make peace with the new. That's how I feel. It's an honest difference of opinion.

Mr. Healy: Aye.

Boy: I just want you to know that we're still friends.

Mr. Healy: You're a good kid.

(The BOY *stands. The mattress spring creaks.)*

Boy: I better get home because I don't like to leave my mother alone these days.

Mr. Healy: I wish you luck.

Boy: I'll see you tomorrow in the shop.

Mr. Healy: I'll see you tomorrow.

(The BOY *opens the door and pauses in the shaft of light that pours into the dark room. A sob almost escapes the old man. He masters it quickly, then turns away.)*

Boy: I'll see you.

(Lights fade, then rise again on the interior of the shop, an hour later. The shop is pitch-black. MR. HEALY *comes in and stands in front of the linotype machine. He raises his hands over his head like a woodchopper. Then he brings his hands down. There is a flash of metal and a horrible crunching sound as the sledgehammer* MR. HEALY *is holding crashes into the linotype machine. Suddenly he begins to cry. The sledgehammer falls from his limp fingers and clatters to the floor. He just stands now, sobbing unashamedly. Lights dim, then rise. It is the next morning. A linotype mechanic is bent over the smashed machine, examining the damage.)*

Mechanic *(exclaiming)*: Boy!

Boss: How much?

Mechanic: It's gonna be at least four hundred bucks. Probably take a week to get this thing fixed.

Mr. Healy: Send me the bill. I'll make you a check. *(to the* LINOTYPIST*)* I'm sorry, mister. It was a foolish thing to do. I must admit this machine makes a good even line of print, and I'm sorry I smashed it up with the sledgehammer.

Linotypist: Well, it's all right — as long as it was the machine and not me.

Mr. Healy *(to the* BOSS*)*: Well, I'll be going then. I got a good bit in the bank. I thought I might take my old lady down to Florida — loll in the sun. More or less enjoy the autumn of my years. See if I can get this ink out from under my nails. Just send me the bill and I'll mail you a check.

Boss: Where are you going?

"He raises his hands over his head like a woodchopper."

Mr. Healy: I'm retiring from the trade.

Boss: Yeah, sure, come on, go to work. *(He throws the apron to* MR. HEALY.*)*

Mr. Healy: Now look here, mister, don't you be so grand or I'll put the sledgehammer to you. I'm sixty-six years old, and if I feel like retiring, I will. I'll finish out the day's work just to help out. But the truth of it is, the trade is beginning to pall on me. I'm weary of this dank little shop and the smell of kerosene is enough to choke a man. Why don't you clean up the shop once in a while — it's getting to be a real Sixth Avenue dump.

(He begins to work. The BOY *stands beside him, smiling and working. Lights dim, rise on the front window with its barely legible, battered old wooden sign, "Emperor Press." The lights fade out.)*

[1] **compositing:** typesetting
[2] **imperiously:** in a domineering or commanding manner
[3] **demeans:** degrades; drags down; lowers in grade or rank
[4] **consignment:** shipped to a dealer who pays only for what he sells
[5] **pica:** a unit of about one-sixth of an inch, used to measure type

A CLOSER LOOK

1. Why does the boss want to install a linotype machine in his shop? What do Mr. Healy's friends think of the idea? What does Mr. Healy himself think of the idea?

2. Why does the boy decide to go back to school? How does this decision effect his relationship with Mr. Healy?

3. Mr. Healy says that "a man's work is the sweetest thing he owns." Do you agree? Explain why or why not.